Principles of vegetable crop production

Principles of vegetable crop production

R. Fordham
Lecturer in Horticulture, Wye College, University of London, UK

and

A. G. Biggs
Head, Department of Horticulture, Hawkesbury Agricultural College, NSW, Australia

COLLINS
8 Grafton Street, London W1

Collins Professional and Technical Books
William Collins Sons & Co. Ltd
8 Grafton Street, London W1X 3LA

First published in Great Britain by
Collins Professional and Technical Books 1985

Distributed in the United States of America
by Sheridan House, Inc.

Copyright © 1985 R. Fordham and A.G. Biggs

British Library Cataloguing in Publication Data
Fordham, R.
   Principles of vegetable crop production.
   1. Vegetables
   I. Title   II. Biggs, A.G.
   635   SB322
ISBN 0–00–383014–4

Printed and bound in Great Britain by
Mackays of Chatham, Kent

Contents

Preface

Vegetable crop production is a multidisciplinary subject covering wide areas of soil science, plant physiology, plant pathology, entomology, engineering, etc. There are many excellent specialist texts dealing with these contributory sciences but relatively few which set out to bring the underlying principles together in a single synthesis. In preparing the present text we have attempted to provide a framework for students of agriculture and horticulture, as well as specialists who wish to turn their attention to the wider application of their subject. By concentrating on the underlying principles we hope we have produced a useful starting point for both groups of readers.

The subject area is wide and cannot be covered in depth within a volume of this size. The pressing need to increase food production while at the same time reducing production costs has led in recent years to an increasing number of innovations and refinements in growing methods. It has not always been possible to deal with such developments in depth but references have been provided at the end of each chapter which should enable the reader to follow up specific topics in more detail.

Any text of this nature owes a great deal to many individuals; some have been acknowledged indirectly by reference to their publications; it is sincerely hoped that the need for brevity has not led to misrepresentation.

We wish to acknowledge the part played by our colleagues and students at Wye College (past ones in Tony Biggs' case as he left to take up a post at Hawkesbury Agricultural College, New South Wales, shortly after embarking on this text). In our discussions with them we have learned much, although the authors accept full responsibility for misconceptions that may have slipped into the text.

Other sources of valuable information include meetings of the National Vegetable Research Station Association and visits to the many growers in Kent who willingly open their doors to periodic invasions from the staff and students of Wye College.

The actual mechanics of producing a final manuscript also owe a great deal to others. Richard Miles and Julian Grover of Collins have made helpful comments and demonstrated extreme patience. Ken Stroud is thanked for his skilful preparation of the text figures. The unenviable task of preparing the final typescript, and several earlier drafts, fell to Maureen Fordham to whom we express our gratitude.

Finally we wish to thank our respective families for their support and encouragement.

R. Fordham
A. G. Biggs

1 Choice of Production Areas and Planning Details

The choice of areas for vegetable production is determined by many factors and both physical and sociological considerations have combined to produce the present distribution pattern. Physical factors such as climate and soils play a major role in determining which species can be grown and the potential productivity of a particular site. Social and economic factors can modify decisions on site choice. The desire to be self sufficient in a particular crop, for example, can have a bearing on site choice which in part overrides otherwise unsuitable site characteristics.

No crop is perfectly matched to its environment and over the centuries man has developed a working compromise in which species have been selected for particular sites, which in turn have been modified to improve the performance of these species. Plant breeders, agronomists and research workers continue to improve the match between crop species and their environment. The first chapter of this text surveys the principal factors determining a site's suitability for vegetable production before outlining the more administrative and managerial considerations relevant to establishing a modern vegetable farm. Later chapters deal with the principles of establishing, growing and ultimately marketing vegetable crops.

Location of population centres

Historically, important market garden areas developed on the outskirts of our major cities. Population centres not only provide a market for produce but also ensure a pool of labour and in earlier times, when horse drawn transport was common, they ensured a supply of organic manure from the stables. Industrial development and the invention of the locomotive modified this pattern as did the physical spread of cities with their increasing populations. Most large towns and cities, however, still retain their associated vegetable production areas and in England, for example, the vegetable producers of the Thames Valley region and the Vale of Evesham continue to be important suppliers of fresh produce for London and Birmingham respectively.

The rapid rise in transport costs during recent years has once more brought the proximity of markets back into the picture as a factor to be considered when selecting a production area. This is particularly so in the instance of relatively low value, bulky crops such as cabbage but can also be an important consideration for highly perishable salad crops which should reach the consumer with minimum delay.

Climatic factors

Although social and economic factors play an important role in the determination of suitable sites for vegetable production, whether or not a particular crop species is grown depends to a major extent on the prevailing climate. Leaving aside glasshouse production, where an artificially controlled environment can be provided to suit the crop, potential yields and the period of supply for the majority of vegetables are determined by climatic variables such as solar radiation, rainfall and temperature. Any attempt to modify these constraints can only be carried out at a cost which at some stage must be passed on to the consumer.

Temperature

At low latitudes, temperatures are rarely limiting and provided that water is available it is possible to grow vegetables throughout the year, although many of the species originating from cooler regions may have a low temperature requirement, as for example in the case of some cultivars of cauliflower where it is required to initiate curding. Similarly, seed production for many biennial crops is not possible without the vernalising stimulus of low temperature.

At higher latitudes, low winter temperatures reduce or stop the growth of vegetables and relatively few can survive the occurrence of frost. In temperate regions, the dates of the last frost in spring and the first frost of winter in many instances therefore define the length of the growing season. Figure 1.1 illustrates the average length of such annual frost free periods throughout Britain although local factors will modify the overall pattern. Proximity to the sea is a major factor limiting the incidence of frost and for this reason the

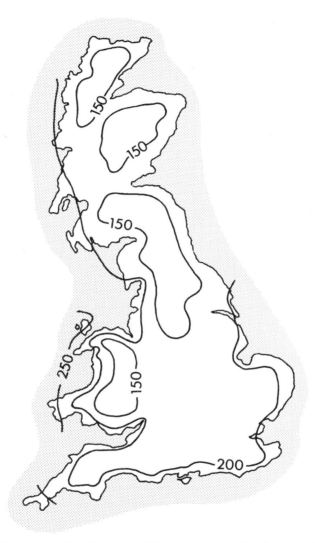

Fig. 1.1. Average length of annual frost free period in days in Britain.

production of frost sensitive winter heading cauliflowers in England is confined largely to coastal areas of Cornwall, Lincolnshire and North East Kent. Similarly, in France, the coastal areas of Brittany are important production areas for this crop.

At the other extreme, high temperatures are required for many crops to reach maturity and ripen. This is particularly so in the case of crops of tropical origin such as sweet corn and tomato, whose productivity in temperate regions is limited by the lower temperatures and shorter duration of the growing season. The commercial production of such crops in Britain is largely confined to the south east where high summer temperatures are recorded. On the basis of a day degree accumulation and historical temperature records it is possible to define areas where economic yields of specific crops are likely to be achieved. This has been carried out for outdoor tomatoes in England and Wales by Barrie and Gray (1980). Onions also benefit from a period of warm dry weather at maturity, although recent harvesting techniques now make it more possible to supply the correct conditions in controlled environment stores.

Rainfall

On and near the equator, rainfall is rarely limiting to crop production and the problems of vegetable growing in these regions stem more frequently from excessive rainfall rather than shortages. In such areas soil erosion, nutrient leaching and the spread of fungal disease all impose serious limitations on growth, and vegetable production may frequently be restricted to a relatively short dry season. At higher latitudes the rainfall pattern becomes more seasonal and the length of the annual dry season increases until between the latitudes of approximately 20–35° in both hemispheres deserts occur and irrigation is essential for any form of crop production.

Beyond these regions annual rainfall increases and vegetable production is once more possible without recourse to irrigation. For maximum growth rainfall should be sufficient to replace the amount of water lost from crops and soil by evapotranspiration. On an annual basis this occurs throughout a large proportion of the temperate regions, although the distribution of rainfall throughout the year can often result in significant deficits developing during the summer months. In Britain, for example, rain is rarely a limiting factor in the west but is frequently so in the south east. If irrigation is to be considered then the site must have access to a ready supply of suitable water at a cost that can be justified in economic terms. The subject of irrigation is dealt with more fully in Chapter 7.

Solar radiation

In the absence of soil moisture deficits, the upper limit to crop productivity is determined by the amount of sunshine or solar energy available for photosynthesis. Much horticultural research has been directed towards increasing the amount of radiation intercepted by plants by increasing both the length of the growing season and the total area of foliage. However, once these factors have been maximised the ultimate determinant of crop yields is solar radiation and, in general terms, this decreases with increasing latitude. Figure 1.2, for example, shows the average daily duration of sunshine received throughout Britain. It is apparent that the

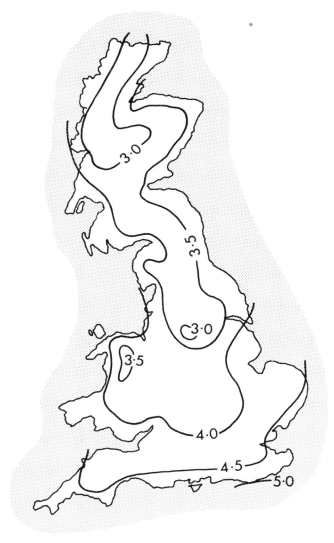

Fig. 1.2. Average number of hours of sunshine per day in Britain.

south of England receives an average of up to five hours a day, in contrast to less than three hours a day in the north of Scotland.

Wind

The air movement produced by light winds can be beneficial by reducing the incidence of both fog and radiation frosts. However, vegetables may suffer from wind damage when grown on exposed sites, where some form of protection will be desirable. Seed beds may dry out rapidly, resulting in poor and irregular seed germination, and in extreme cases both soil and seeds can be blown from the fields. Crops may be physically damaged during strong winds, resulting in both reduced yields and lower quality. Runner beans are particularly susceptible to such damage for, in addition to being blown from their supports in strong winds, even moderate winds will cause sufficient twisting and bruising of pods to render them unmarketable.

Some regions of the world suffer from the regular occurrence of damaging winds, for example the cold dry northerly Mistral of the Rhône Valley in France, and the Harmatten which brings dry desert air down to the more humid regions of West Africa.

Protection from damaging winds can be achieved by using either natural windbreaks, composed of suitable tree species, or by hessian or synthetic materials such as plastic, but this has to be considered against the loss of production area and the cost of planting or installation. It must also be appreciated that natural windbreaks will compete for soil water and nutrients and any type will cause some degree of shading. The physical aspects of protection from damaging winds have received considerable attention and it has been shown that the optimum permeability of a windbreak should be approximately 50%. Impermeable structures can cause severe turbulence resulting in increased wind speed and crop damage. Windbreaks orientated at right angles to the prevailing wind direction can have beneficial effects on crop growth down wind for a distance of up to fifteen times the height of the windbreak. In recent years there has been a trend towards hedge removal to increase field size to facilitate mechanisation of farming operations. Such a trend is not without risk and due consideration should be given to the exposure of a site and the potential damage that can occur as a consequence of erosion, particularly in areas with light soils.

An alternative to permanent windbreaks is the use of inter-cropping where, for example, a tall crop such as maize can be planted to provide protection for a shorter species. Another useful technique for reducing wind erosion on light soils is to incorporate narrow bands of straw into the soil so that it stands up vertically between the crop rows to form miniature shelterbreaks. Special machinery has been developed for introducing straw into soil in this manner.

Windbreaks can also affect the distribution and activity of insect populations and one of the benefits of providing shelter for runner beans is the resultant increase in crop brought about by increased pollination by bees. A wide range of trees and shrubs can be used to provide shelter although some are associated with specific insect pests and should therefore be avoided. Poplars (*Populus spp.*) for example act as an alternative host for the lettuce root aphid (*Pemphigus bursarius*) and willows (*Salix spp.*) harbour willow carrot aphids (*Cavariella aegopodii*).

Altitude

The effects of latitude are significantly modified by height above sea level, since increasing rainfall and reducing air temperatures occur with increasing altitude. On average, a 100 m increase in altitude is associated with a 0.6°C drop in temperature which, in temperate regions, may result in a poorer environment for vegetable production. In the tropics however the cooler moister conditions of high plateau regions, such as the highlands of Kenya, can provide better conditions for many vegetables than the hotter and drier lowlands.

Aspect and slope

The microclimate of a site is greatly influenced by its slope and aspect. In the northern hemisphere a south facing slope warms up more quickly in the spring, giving it advantages in terms of earliness of production. In the past many small but intensive market gardens were located in such favoured sites but increasing trends towards mechanisation have reduced the advantages of such locations. For modern, farm scale production of vegetables large flat sites are to be preferred although a slight slope towards the south will still offer advantages over an equivalent area facing north in terms of radiation intercepted. The problems of water runoff and soil erosion increase significantly with steepening slopes.

Cold air is heavier than warm air and under still conditions will move downhill to produce a pool of cold air at the bottom of the slope. This can result in a frost pocket which limits crop production and such sites should be avoided. The problem can be further aggravated by the presence of badly sited windbreaks and hedges which may prevent the cold air draining from a field although such problems can be alleviated by removing a section of the barrier at its lowest point.

Soil

The most suitable soils for vegetable production are usually defined as deep, fertile, well drained, light to medium loams. Well drained organic soils are also suitable although in practice most vegetable crops can be grown on a much wider range of soil types. Some degree of soil amelioration is always possible but it is well to be aware of particular crop requirements when selecting a site for specialised production. Brussels sprouts, for example, generally grow better on heavier loams and will tend to produce loose sprouts on the lighter textured soils. Root crops, especially carrots, are more suited to sandy soils and the presence of stones is particularly disadvantageous. Water availability is important for all vegetables but many are susceptible to even short periods of moisture shortage. Celery, for example, is particularly suited to moisture retaining peat soils. It is possible to correct nutrient levels and pH to suit particular crops but texture is more difficult to modify.

Excessive soil water can be as harmful to plant growth as insufficient water, as it reduces the availability of oxygen to roots. Poor drainage can result from many causes including the presence of impervious layers in the subsoil or by the combination of a heavy textured clay with high rainfall. Whatever the cause, good drainage is essential for vegetable production and if necessary it should be improved by either subsoiling or installing some form of drainage system.

In areas that have been previously cropped there is always the risk of residual soil borne pests and diseases. In some instances these may be short lived and easily reduced by cultural and chemical control methods. However others present more of a problem and club root (*Plasmodiophora brassicae*), for example, can survive in soil in the absence of its brassica host for at least five years. Similar problems may occur with eelworms or nematodes and in such instances the presence of these pests may detract considerably from a site's suitability as a basis for intensive cropping.

Planning the enterprise

So far we have considered the physical characteristics of a site in terms of its suitability for vegetable production and many of the points raised will be taken up in greater detail in later chapters. Given the necessary technical back-up it is relatively easy to determine whether or not a crop will grow on a particular site and to estimate with a reasonable degree of accuracy the average yields that might be expected. However, the decision on the type of enterprise and the crops to be grown depends on a far more complex web of inter-related factors, many of which extend beyond the scope of the present book.

Successful marketing is one of the more important aspects and is dealt with in Chapter 9. It is becoming increasingly important to establish a market outlet for a crop before growing it. The location of roads, railways and ports for export outlets are all factors to consider in deciding on the suitability of a site and the range of crops to be grown.

Labour availability is a particularly important consideration and labour intensive crops such as runner beans cannot readily be grown on the same scale as, for example, carrots and onions, where larger areas may be necessary to justify the investment in machinery. Cropping schedules will also need to be planned carefully to even out peaks in labour requirement throughout the year. The most labour demanding step in vegetable production is usually that of harvesting and the use of casual labour will often prove a satisfactory method for coping with the inevitable peaks in demand. However, it is also desirable to retain a core of skilled labour and some crops may be included in an enterprise in order to provide suitable employment during off-peak periods. However specialised a grower may become, he will always find a benefit from including alternative crops to form part of a rotation, thus reducing the build-up of specific pest and disease problems. Many arable farmers have chosen to include vegetables as break crops in cereal based enterprises.

Investment capital is an essential prerequisite to any successful enterprise. Grant aid in some form or other is often available to growers, although the form that this takes will differ from country to country and from year to year. Government sponsored advisory services are generally available to provide details of such schemes which may for example cover such aspects as improving land drainage or assistance for the provision of farm buildings. It is frequently the policy of governments to promote the development of particular regions and in such instances the assistance provided can sometimes compensate for shortcomings that would otherwise exist in a particular location.

A grower must also make himself aware of legislation that affects the way in which a site may be utilised. He is not free to use a site in any way he wishes and, particularly in areas of outstanding natural beauty or significant recreational value, there may be severe, but usually justifiable, constraints placed on land use for crop production. It may, for example, be difficult or even impossible to obtain permission to built a vegetable store on site. Government legislation covers many areas such as safety, protection of the environment and conditions of employment.

In addition to providing up to date information on government legislation, advisory services are usually available as a technical back-up to growers in relation to the numerous problems that may arise in vegetable production. In England, the national Agricultural Development and Advisory Service (A.D.A.S.) provides scientific, professional and technical advice free to growers on request. Its officers have ready access to a range of analytical and diagnostic services, such as soil analysis and pest identification, and in some instances these are routinely available direct to growers at nominal charges. The service also carries out research and development work on its own stations and also in collaboration with, for example, university departments and individual growers.

One factor having an important bearing on the success of a vegetable producing enterprise is that of farm size. One approach available to a grower for realising a higher income is to extend production to a larger area of land. However, although this possibility should be borne in mind when selecting a site, the alternative of intensifying production in order to increase income per unit area is often more appropriate. The area of land in the world suitable for food production is limited and can only be significantly extended at considerable cost. In order to feed the world's increasing population and to enhance the quality of life, not only in terms of food but also by providing space for recreation, it is essential that more intensive systems of production are adopted. There is considerable potential for increasing vegetable yields but it is important that such increases are sustainable and that, for example, deterioration of soil conditions do not lead to a longer term decline in production.

To make decisions, a grower has a constant need for data.

Mention has already been made of the value of the advisory services in providing external data, including technical aspects on the suitability of new chemicals for pest control, for example. Other sources of external data on both technical and economic matters will include grower co-operatives and private consultants. Ultimately, however, a grower will have to evaluate these external data in terms of the internal data available on his own particular enterprise. He will need to know both his expenditure on raw materials and labour and the return from sales of his separate products. He will also find it useful to have information on the development of his individual crops from planting to maturity. To a large extent the development of the computer and associated programs has made it possible for the grower to store and retrieve large quantities of data for use in decision making. By repeated 'runs' of a program he is able to compare the likely consequences of varying inputs and in doing so increase his awareness of the options available. The collection and use of data form an integral component of running a successful vegetable farm.

It should by now be apparent that there is no simple formula for selecting a site for vegetable production, depending as it does on so many interrelated scientific, economic and social factors. For similar reasons, in spite of the availability of a wealth of technical data, it is impossible to provide a recipe for the successful production of specific vegetable crops. Vegetable production, like most activities, cannot be learnt from a book although it is hoped that the following chapters will provide a framework of principles on which practical experience can be built.

References and further reading

Barrie, I.A. and Gray, D. (1980) 'Mapping areas of England and Wales suitable for outdoor tomato production.' *A.D.A.S. Quarterly Review*, **38**, 138–144.

Chandler, T.J. and Gregory, S. eds. (1976) *The Climate of the British Isles*. London: Longman.

Folley, R.R.W. (1973) *Intensive Crop Economics*. London: Heinemann.

Hardy, F.S. and Watson, G.D. (1982) *The Complete Guide to Commercial Vegetable Growing*. London: Frederick Muller.

Harper, F. (1983) *Principles of Arable Crop Production*. London: Granada Publishing.

Hudson, J.P. (1977) 'Plants and the weather'. In *Environmental Effects on Crop Physiology*, eds. J.J. Landsberg and C.V. Cutting. London: Academic Press, pp. 1–20.

Milthorpe, F.L. and Moorby, J. (1981) *An Introduction to Crop Physiology*. 2nd edn. Cambridge: University Press.

Ministry of Agriculture, Fisheries and Food (1967) *Horticulture in Britain. Part 1. Vegetables*. London: H.M.S.O.

Ministry of Agriculture, Fisheries and Food (1968) *Shelterbreaks for Farmland*. London: H.M.S.O.

Ministry of Agriculture, Fisheries and Food (1979) *Maximising Yields of Crops*. London: H.M.S.O.

Ministry of Agriculture, Fisheries and Food (1980) *Farm Planning by Computer*. (Reference Book 419). London: H.M.S.O.

Ministry of Agriculture, Fisheries and Food (1983) *At the Farmer's Service*. London: M.A.F.F.

Smith, L.P. (1976) *The Agricultural Climate of England and Wales*. M.A.F.F. Tech. Bull. No. 35. London: H.M.S.O.

Spedding, C.R.W. *ed*. (1981) *Vegetable Productivity*. Symposia of Institute of Biology No. 25. London: Macmillan.

2   Soils and Vegetable Production

Many factors have been shown to influence the type of vegetable production which takes place in a particular area. Climate, proximity and type of markets, availability of labour and other resources, size of holding, pattern of farming and family tradition are important but the type and properties of the available soils will have a major influence on the pattern of production and on the crops which can be grown.

Soil properties and cropping

Soil properties may be classified as either inherent or acquired, although there may be some overlap between the two groups. The inherent properties of our soils have developed over millions of years during the climatic and geological processes which transformed parent rocks into the thin, cultivated layer of land in which we now grow crops. Such properties include soil texture (i.e. sands, loams, silts, clays, etc.); the relative thicknesses of various soil horizons (i.e. topsoil, subsoil, etc.); soil structure; drainage and water-holding capacity and the presence or absence of stones, flints and hard pan zones which may form an obstruction to root growth. An approximate assessment of these properties can be determined relatively easily by eye or touch but it is difficult and expensive to make any major alterations. Some small-scale amelioration may be possible but one of the important principles of crop production must be to assess inherent soil properties and match them with suitable crops. Growing a crop in an unsuitable soil will usually create considerable technical and management problems.

Acquired soil properties are more easily changed and include nutrient status; organic matter content; soil reaction (pH) and certain aspects of drainage and water retention. Nutrient and pH levels can be determined accurately by laboratory analyses and the results used in conjunction with the inherent properties to decide the suitability for vegetable growing.

The inherent and acquired properties of a particular soil will also influence the intensity with which the land can be cropped. Intensive production of vegetables demands 'high input–high output' systems which include maximum cultivation and cropping of the soil. Rapid turn round between crops is essential and there is rarely time for the land to be fallowed. The economic pressures associated with this type of production can easily lead to over-use of the soil, damage to soil structure and a consequent deterioration of intensive potential.

Highly intensive production units are usually small in size with considerable inputs of labour, often whole family groups, and only limited use of mechanised equipment. They contrast with the typical large, farm-sized unit where capital, in the form of machines, replaces labour and where fewer crops are grown. The intensive small-holdings or market gardens tend to be clustered around population centres and include such areas as the Vale of Evesham near Birmingham; the Kikuyu 'shambas' near Nairobi in Kenya and the holdings farmed by Greek, Italian, Jugoslav and other ethnic minority groups on the fringes of the Australian cities of Melbourne and Sydney. The continuing spread of urbanisation consumes market garden land while the labour force may be attracted to potentially higher paid and more socially acceptable employment away from the land.

Regular supplies of fresh produce and earliness of production are fundmental requirements for intensive growers. Regular and continuous supplies of vegetables are possible from soils which are easily and quickly cultivated between crops and which allow plant growth to extend over a long period. Coarse-textured, large-particled sandy soils are, therefore, much more suitable than clays and other soils with a predominance of small-sized particles. Earliness is also associated with those soils which allow free drainage of water and rapid increases in soil temperature at the beginning of the season. Silts and clays retain water around the particles much longer and, while this may be a desirable feature in times of moisture stress and drought, soil temperatures tend to be lower and the soils are difficult to cultivate until some drying out takes place. Free passage of water through the soil profile, coupled with unhindered drainage away from the water table, also influences plant growth in the wet soil conditions often found during winter periods in temperate countries or after torrential rainfall in tropical climates. Finely textured silts and clays or soils with impeded drainage are more likely to become waterlogged so that normal respiration of roots and soil fauna is reduced and anaerobic conditions develop. Roots are killed and the aerial parts of the plant turn yellow. The death of absorptive roots will reduce water uptake and cause plants to wilt even when normal soil conditions are restored.

Production of vegetables on a farm scale allows the soil to be treated less intensively with periods of fallowing, grass leys or green manure cropping being introduced into the farming programme. Labour inputs per unit area (or per unit of output) are usually lower than on small-holdings and a high level of mechanisation is required to cope with the large areas of individual crops. This approach to production is typified by the growing of green peas for processing. Farm scale production rarely involves more than one vegetable crop per year from a particular piece of land whereas intensive production requires much shorter rotations and more concentrated use of the land.

Soil texture

The relative proportions of sand, silt, clay and organic matter particles determine soil texture and the properties associated with different textures will influence the growth and development of plants. Table 2.1 shows the equivalent sizes of various soil particles and also indicates the approximate pore space to be found in the corresponding soils. In practice there is considerable variation in the total porosity of a soil since it depends not only on particle size but also on the extent of packing and aggregation.

Accurate determinations of the sand, silt, clay and organic matter fractions will require mechanical and chemical analyses in a laboratory but approximate determinations can be carried out in the field by rubbing a small quantity of moist soil between thumb and

Table 2.1 Particle sizes and pore spaces

Particle	International symbol	Equivalent diameter (mm)	Approximate pore space in predominant soil (% of soil volume)
Stones and gravel	G	More than 2.0	
Coarse sand	CS	2.0–0.2	30
Fine sand	FS	0.2–0.05	
Silt	Z	0.05–0.002	
Clay	C	Less than 0.002	More than 50

forefinger. Grittiness indicates a sandy soil; silkiness shows a predominance of silt or organic matter while clays become polished with continual rubbing and are very sticky when wet. Figure 2.1 indicates the relative proportions of sand, silt and clay present in the range of soils recognised by the United States Soil Survey Department.

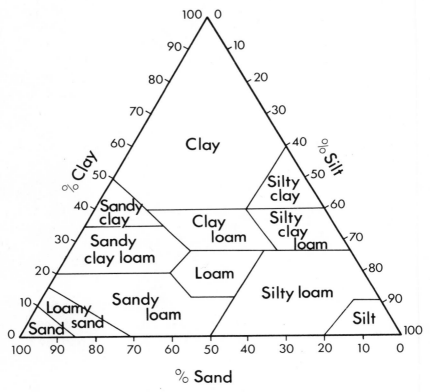

Fig. 2.1. Soil textural classes. United States soil survey classification.

Sandy soils

The predominance of relatively large, angular particles in sandy soils ensures good drainage and rapid soil temperature increase but their moisture-holding properties are poor. Organic matter and nutrient levels in such soils are inherently low. The higher temperature and greater aeration of sandy soils cause rapid microbiological breakdown of organic matter. Freshly applied material soon breaks down and disappears so that sandy soils are sometimes referred to as 'hungry'. Regular, heavy applications are required before any long-term improvement is observed in organic matter status.

Low inherent organic matter levels and rapid breakdown of applied material, coupled with the frequent cultivations to which sands are often subjected, can result in soil structure defects on these soils. Sand particles come from the breakdown of quartz (SiO_2) and contribute very little to plant nutrition. Sand particles are too large and angular to allow adsorption of nutrients and herbicides onto their surface. Nutrients which have a high water solubility are readily leached from the soils into the ground water where they may cause problems when the water is re-used for agricultural or industrial purposes.

Soil-acting herbicides are not adsorbed by sand particles and are free, but frequently insoluble, in the soil water from where they may damage particularly sensitive crop plants. Great care is needed when using soil-acting herbicides, such as simazine, on coarse-particled sandy soils and it may be necessary to reduce the quantity of herbicide used. Further protection can be obtained with transplanted crops by treating the plant roots with an absorbent material before planting. Allott (1968) suggested the use of activated charcoal as a pre-planting protective root dip for brassicas to reduce the risks involved in using post-planting applications of partially phytotoxic soil-acting herbicides.

Irrigation is essential on sandy soils which can then be highly productive. The additional silt, clay and organic matter in sandy loams have a moderating effect and such soils are more useful for vegetable production. Sands and sandy loams have the big advantages that they are easy to cultivate and can soon be worked after wet weather.

Loams

The term 'loam' is usually applied to the horticulturally more desirable types of soil and indicates a mixture of various particle sizes. Thus a sandy loam has silt, clay and organic matter particles but is dominated by the sand fraction. Loams are intermediate or general-purpose soils and, with good management, should combine the workability properties of sands with the better moisture retention, nutritional status and soil structure of silts and clays.

Silts

Silts have a larger proportion of small-sized particles which contribute to undesirable properties such as 'capping' and slow drainage. Planting or sowing tilths are produced with a fine surface and the silt particles pack very closely together. Heavy rain or irrigation cause the particles to run together and, if the sun or wind cause rapid drying, a surface crust or cap may be formed which does not crack as it dries (McIntyre, 1958).

This impervious layer interferes with aeration, water penetration and seedling emergence. Small seeded crops, such as lettuce, carrots and onions, are badly affected while the shoots from larger seeded vegetables such as legumes, are able to push through the cap. Sale and Harrison (1964) showed reduced emergence of lettuce, beetroot and spinach seedlings when capping was caused by post-sowing irrigation and subsequent drying. Emergence is not affected if the cap remains wet. Capping is less severe if post-sowing irrigation is done with small droplets and good emergence can always be restored if capped surfaces are broken by light cultivation as soon as they dry. The problem can be reduced by deliberately minimising cultivations in order to produce coarse tilths on silty soils, or by using some form of chemical stabilisation of the soil surface. Krilium (the trade name of a Monsanto Chemical Company material) was recommended as a soil stabiliser by Martin et al. in 1952 but it has not been widely used. Cellulose xanthate was patented as a soil conditioner in America in 1956 and now shows considerable promise. A 1% solution is sprayed over the drilled rows and there are no indications of seedling damage since the cellulose xanthate is adsorbed onto soil particles (Menefee and Hautala, 1978).

Silt soils are inherently more fertile than sands and the particle size confers properties which cause nutrients and soil-acting residual herbicides to be adsorbed and more efficiently used. Timing of cultivations is more critical than for sands and consequently silty soils are rarely used for very intensive crop production.

Clays and clay loams

These soils have a greater proportion of small-sized particles and are very sticky when wet but extremely hard and cloddy when dry. Clay particles are much more active chemically and biologically than the sand or silt fractions. An internal plate-like structure and large surface area per unit volume gives the particles considerable adsorptive properties which influence soil structure, moisture retention and nutrient and herbicide activity. Clay particles are also an important source of such plant nutrients as potassium, magnesium, calcium, iron and sodium.

These soils retain a high percentage of moisture and require very skilful management in order to maintain their structure. Timing of cultivations is particularly important and it is usually necessary to improve drainage. Given appropriate management they may be used for vegetable growing but are more suited to extensive systems.

Peaty and organic soils

Soils with a high percentage of organic matter are often termed 'peats'. They are dark coloured and usually rich in nitrogenous material but low in nutrients such as potassium. Peats will absorb large quantities of water but are extremely difficult to re-wet once they have dried out. The soil reaction tends to be acid and heavy liming may be necessary to raise the pH to a satisfactory level. Continuous cultivation increases the exposure of peat to air and encourages rapid breakdown of the organic matter so that these soils are gradually disappearing in areas of intensive cultivation, heavy irrigation and high temperatures. Peats are easily cultivated even after very heavy rain or irrigation. They are ideal for root crops, such as carrots and parsnips, which can be lifted cleanly and with the minimum of damage. The upward movement of water from the water table can be important in peat soils and this makes them ideal for growing celery, which responds to a continually available supply of moisture.

Calcareous soils

Calcareous soils which have formed over limestone or chalk are often very thin with perhaps as little as 20–30 cm of topsoil. They dry out very quickly and generous irrigation programmes rarely produce satisfactory crop growth. The soil reaction (pH) is high but for the majority of vegetables this is more acceptable than an acid condition. Deep, chalky soils are more useful but when wet are very sticky and difficult to cultivate.

Soil structure

Soil particles are gradually bonded together by the combined activity of chemical and/or physical reactions and biological organisms. The bonding process is influenced by soil texture (particle size) and helped by the action of colloidal cementing agents (iron and aluminium hydroxides) and soil organic matter. Granular crumbs are formed initially which subsequently amalgamate into larger aggregates with a blocky, plate-like or prismatic appearance.

A well structured soil, for example one that has recently been cultivated from long-term grassland, will have a good crumb appearance at the surface which gradually gives way to a blocky, fissured structure further down the profile. Such a soil will have approximately 50% soil particles, 20% air and 30% water at field capacity. Worm channels and cracks allow the free movement of roots, drainage water and air so that plants are evenly and adequately supplied with oxygen, water and nutrients. Cultivations are easy and roots are able to penetrate considerable distances to make better use of valuable nutrient and moisture reserves, an important factor in dry years and periods of drought. Well structured soils are more able to withstand the cultivations required to produce a stable and penetrable drilling or planting tilth. The profiles of well structured soils are uniformly coloured without zones of compaction, or areas of colour mottling.

Some soil types are naturally of a weaker structure than others and require particular care. High proportions of fine sand and silt are associated with poor structure while large amounts of clay and organic matter particles contibute to good structure and stability.

The profiles of poorly structured soils often show mottled colouring and compacted layers or pans while pockets of undecomposed organic matter may give off the unpleasant smell of hydrogen sulphide and be surrounded by blue and grey colourations in the soil. Such soils are difficult to cultivate and the drilling or planting tilths are unstable and collapse into an amorphous powder. Root penetration is poor and crops suffer particularly in periods of drought. Plant growth and yield are reduced since the root environment is suboptimal.

Maintenance of soil structure

Good soil structure is encouraged by sensible husbandry with particular attention being paid to drainage, cultivation and the addition of organic matter.

Many soil structural problems are the result of poor soil drainage. Inadequate surface penetration and slow drainage through the profile cause water to stand in or on the surface layers. Under such conditions the use of heavy machinery, for such operations as root crop harvesting, will cause rapid structural breakdown especially in unstable soils such as silts. Poor drainage may also result from the presence of compacted layers or pans which impede vertical water movement. These may be broken up by appropriate cultivation or subsoiling when the soil is dry. Although incorporation of organic matter and trash into soils is beneficial for improving structure, under poorly drained anaerobic conditions it is likely to produce hydrogen sulphide toxic to root growth.

Ploughing when the soil is too wet causes rapid deterioration of soil structure. The formation of plough pans begins when the plough share runs through wet soil and produces thin horizontal smears which effectively seal vertical pores and fissures in the profile. Water cannot pass through the smeared zone and the soil above becomes successively wetter so that, eventually, waterlogged and anaerobic conditions develop. Free soil particles are washed down onto the smeared surface where they accumulate to form a compacted layer or pan. In time the particles may become cemented together by iron compounds to form an extremely hard barrier, impervious to both water and plant roots.

The continual use of rotovators at the same depth in wet soils also produces smearing and the soil structure is further damaged by excessively high rotor speeds which shatter soil crumbs and particles.

It is important that soils are ploughed and cultivated when the land is sufficiently dry. Optimum conditions do not occur frequently but the most successful farmers are those who appreciate the dangers of untimely cultivations and who have sufficient machinery to deal with operations at the most suitable time. Forced cultivations, such as seedbed preparation, usually require over-use of machines and are likely to damage the soil structure.

Soil smearing can also occur during planting. Transplanting machines make slits through the soil, the sides of which can smear in wet conditions, thus impeding the penetration of plant roots.

Cultivations should be kept to a minimum but, since intensive producers must change rapidly from one crop to the next and since the stability of structure varies with soil type, it follows that 'high input–high output' systems of vegetable growing should take place on well structured soils.

The maintenance of soil structure is very dependent upon the organic matter and humus fraction of the soil, which should be kept as high as possible. Root growth is particularly important in this respect and soil structure is more likely to remain stable when fibrous rooted plants are grown rather than those with coarse or tap roots. Brassicas and legumes are, for example, better than bulb onions, carrots and beetroot in this respect. The fibrous roots of grass are particularly useful for building up the crumb structure of soils.

Almost any cultural operation aimed at stimulating plant growth will, via its effect on encouraging the development of vigorous and biologically active roots, contribute to maintaining soil structure. Nitrogenous fertilisers are valuable in this respect and even peas, which rarely respond to nitrogen on well structured fertile soil, show responses in the early part of the growing season on poorly structured soils.

Similarly, by increasing the pH of acid soils, liming will improve soil structure by encouraging biological activity, root growth and particle aggregation. Irrigation too has a role to play since adequate soil moisture is essential to the development of biological activity and hence structure. Care should be taken however since the application of large water droplets can easily shatter the crumbs of weakly structured soils. In practice, irrigation systems ideally should be designed to apply small droplets and, particularly when there is little crop canopy to break the impact of droplets on the soil, application rates should not exceed 6 mm per hour.

Soil organic matter

Stress has been placed on the role of organic matter in maintaining soil structure. There are two components of soil organic matter. Fibrous remains of plant residues are readily recognisable but humus is a dark, decomposed material which improves the physical, chemical and biological condition of the soil. Well balanced and healthy plant growth is more readily achieved on soils with adequate organic matter and there are suggestions that useful growth promoting substances may also be present.

Organic matter accumulates naturally in undisturbed soils which are covered in vegetation and build-up is particularly favoured under grass so that recently ploughed grassland soils may have up to 10% organic matter.

In addition to its contribution in maintaining structure, organic matter has an important role in the retention and availability of soil moisture and nutrients. The fibrous material will contain complex organic nitrogenous compounds which are gradually broken down by micro-organisms to release nitrogen which, in the form of nitrates, becomes available for plant growth. Decomposition will also release other plant nutrients such as phosphorus, potassium, calcium, magnesium and trace elements. Decomposed humus has colloidal properties and helps to retain released or applied nutrients, improve nutrient availability and influence the rate of degradation of soil acting residual herbicides (Walker, 1977).

Under normal vegetable crop production systems the organic matter disappears slowly but replacement and build-up are equally slow. The loss of organic matter is accelerated by high temperatures, improved aeration and liming. Soils which have been cultivated for several decades may only have 2% organic matter, with coarse sandy soils likely to have the lowest levels. Most of the organic matter is in the cultivated zones of the soil with very small amounts in the subsoil. Once the levels have fallen to 1% or 2%, vast quantities of organic materials are needed to correct the situation. Regular applications of bulky animal manures at the rate of 50 tonnes per hectare used to be common in Britain but dwindling supplies and rising costs of both manure and transport have reduced the practice. Maintenance of soil structure is still vital, however, and a range of organic materials and methods of conservation are used.

Grass leys

Short-term grass leys with vigorous root systems may have beneficial effects after as little as one year but long-term crops are needed when the organic matter levels have become very low. Three year leys can increase the level by 0.2% while a ten year grass break may give a 0.6% improvement. Increases are slow and shortage of land may limit the use of grass leys. The technique is not suitable for intensively cropped small-holdings but is useful on large scale production units where vegetables are only part of a mixed farming business.

Farmyard manures and other organic residues

Farmyard manures and other sources of organic matter are included in this section in view of their contribution to improving soil structure although reference is also made to their contribution to inorganic nutrition. The value of good farmyard manure as a soil conditioner has been demonstrated regularly over the years by Haworth (1965). It is estimated that 1 tonne of good farmyard manure will add about 150–200 kg of organic matter. It is impossible to generalise about the nutrient content of farmyard manure since it depends on the source, the method of storage and the final condition of the material. An average sample will have about 0.6% N, 0.3% P_2O_5 and 0.7% K_2O, although not all of these nutrients are immediately available for plant uptake, the nitrogen particularly is often a constituent of complex organic molecules. We may estimate, however, that a 10 tonne dressing of average farmyard manure will supply 15 kg N, 20 kg P_2O_5 and 40 kg K_2O. Animal manures are also available in liquid form as slurries whose value depends on the time of application. Ten thousand litres of undiluted pig slurry will supply about 44 kg N, 11 kg P_2O_5 and 22 kg K_2O. Winter or heavy rainfall will leach out some of the nitrogen but the phosphorus and potassium are unaffected.

Poultry manure is more concentrated than other animal manures and must be used carefully since some of the nitrogen will be present as raw ammonia and can damage crop plants. A 10 tonne dressing should supply 110 kg N, 90 kg P_2O_5 and 90 kg K_2O.

Various types of straw can be used as soil additives but the amounts of nutrients provided are likely to be small. Straw can be a useful conditioner however, especially when the soil structure is very poor. Raw straw is broken down by bacterial processes which deplete the soil nitrogen reserves. This temporary shortage is overcome by incorporating 10 kg of nitrogen with every tonne of dry straw.

Leafy residues which remain in the field after cabbage, Brussels sprouts, cauliflower and other crops make very little difference to soil organic matter levels since the majority is lost during decomposition. Collection and composting of the residues may be more successful and the recycling of resources is an issue which must receive more attention as primary resource costs continue to rise.

Sewage sludges may be readily available but will have less effect on physical structure than strawy organic manures. They are relatively low in nitrogen but rich in phosphorus while potassium is virtually absent. Raw sludge is best avoided, particularly for use in conjunction with salad crop production, since it usually has an unpleasant smell and may contain disease organisms. Digested sludge is a more convenient material to deal with and may be available as either a liquid or cake, a 10 tonne dressing of which will supply about 35 kg N and 80 kg P_2O_5. Care should be taken in choosing a source however, since sewage may also contain quantities of heavy metals such as nickel, zinc, chromium and copper which can have phytotoxic effects on crop plants.

Other sources of organic matter that may be locally available include town refuse, spent hops from breweries and spent mushroom compost. The latter material has a similar composition to farmyard manure but also contains lime from the casing material.

In coastal regions seaweeds may also be available although high transport costs prevent its use further inland. Seaweed has nitrogen and organic matter levels similar to farmyard manure but fresh material also contains considerable quantities of sodium chloride which may damage some vegetables and reduce soil stability. Seaweed derivatives are also sold for foliar feeding and contain useful quantities of important trace elements. Peats are expensive and are rarely used as a soil conditioner on anything other than small intensive holdings. They contain very few nutrients but they can improve water holding and soil structure.

Green manure

The technique of green manuring is more applicable to extensive, farm-scale enterprises where there is a space and time to grow the required crops and plough them in. Green manure crops such as mustard (*Brassica alba*), rape (*Brassica napus*) and Italian rye grass (*Lolium multiflorum*) only occupy the ground for relatively short periods but they prevent saleable vegetables being grown. A tonne of green manure dry matter will add about 0.1% to the soil organic matter but very little is converted to residual humus.

Soil depth

The best soils for vegetables are likely to be those with a good layer of dark brown top soil overlying a further 60 cm to 1 m of uniformly brown subsoil. Soils with mixtures of colours and mottling in their profile should be avoided as these features indicate wetness and/or anaerobic conditions either now or in the past.

Deep soils are most desirable but some vegetable crops are more shallow rooted than others. Most lettuce roots for example are confined to the top 30 cm of the soil profile whereas those of Brussels sprouts may extend to 1 m in depth. The benefits of deep, unimpeded soils are most obvious in dry conditions when even shallow-rooted crops will grow down for the deeper moisture reserves.

The topsoil is regularly cultivated but the subsoil tends to be undisturbed. Deeper cultivations will mix the upper subsoil layers with the topsoil and increase the depth of worked soil available for unrestricted root growth. The process of deep cultivation was traditionally carried out by the process of double digging in which both the topsoil and the layer immediately beneath it were dug without reversing their relative positions. More recently this technique has been mechanised with the Wye College double digger (Anon., 1975). The machine rotovates the bottom of the previously ploughed furrow and then turns the next slice over onto the rotovated layers. This method of cultivation has been shown by Rowse and Stone (1980) to produce significant increases in growth and yield of potatoes, summer cabbage, beetroot and broad beans. Larger volumes of soil are available for roots to exploit for nutrient and water uptake. Frequency of irrigation application can also be reduced when the potential rooting depth is increased.

Detailed examinations of soil profiles are best carried out in pits at least 1.5 m deep, although a preliminary indication can be obtained using a soil auger, when the core samples will show any colour variations or compacted layers.

Soil drainage

Surface penetration and movement of water down the profile take place rapidly in well structured soils. Drainage problems are indicated by mottled colours in the soil profile and can occur in low lying areas which collect water from the surrounding land. Under such conditions the water table may be close to the surface and major drainage works involving ditch deepening, tile draining and perhaps pumping will be required to lower the level.

Poor drainage can also be caused by hard, compacted layers or pans in the soil and is improved by subsoiling which breaks up the compaction. Severe panning causes an artificially high water table to perch on the compacted layer, below which the soil is dry. Subsoiling under dry conditions produces a system of deep vertical cracks which break up the compacted layers and assist the movement of water, air and plant roots.

The presence of poor drainage may be apparent at the soil surface, particularly in instances where the passage of machinery during wet conditions has further damaged its structure, thus

aggravating the problem. Poor drainage is likely to cause repercuss-
ions at each stage of crop development from establishment to
harvest. Wet soils will not only be inappropriate for the production
of a suitable tilth for sowing but they will be slow to warm up in the
spring, leading to delayed and patchy germination. This in turn is
likely to be followed by restricted root growth thus adversely
affecting both fertiliser and water uptake with the increased risk of
wilting during periods of dry weather. With variations in germination and seedling emergence, followed by impeded growth, low
yields and poor quality of resultant produce are inevitable. Diseases
may also contribute to losses for many, including club root of
brassicas (*Plasmodiophora brassicae*) and foot rots of legumes
(*Fusarium spp.*), are more prevalent in wet soils. At the final stage,
harvesting, particularly of root crops, may be delayed or become
impossible without significant losses on poorly drained land.

Vegetable crops vary in their sensitivity to poor drainage but
damage symptoms are likely to occur where there are less than 45
cm of freely drained soil. For most crops, 60 cm of unrestricted soil
are adequate but care must be exercised where there is a high water
table for, particularly in the case of fine-particled soils such as clays,
water can rise as much as 50 cm by capillary action.

Soil reaction (pH)

The acidity or alkalinity of soils is expressed on a pH scale based on
the hydrogen ion concentration within the soil water solution:

$$pH = \log_{10} \frac{1}{H^+}$$

On this scale neutral is represented by a value of pH 7 while values 0
to 7 are decreasingly acid and 7 to 14 are increasingly alkaline. The
scale has a tenfold change in relative acidity or alkalinity for each
unit change in pH. In practice, the range experienced in soils is
rarely outside the pH range 3 to 9 and the majority usually lie
between 4.5 and 7.5.

Most soils used for vegetable production become gradually more
acid as calcium is lost from the soil as a consequence of leaching by
rain and irrigation. Such losses occur at a greater rate in sandy soils
than in the more finely textured soils. The process is accelerated by
the use of certain nitrogenous fertilisers with ammonium nitrate
(NH_4NO_3) using up about 300 kg of ground limestone ($CaCO_3$) for

every 100 kg N applied and sulphate of ammonia ($(NH_4)_2SO_4$) using twice the amount. Calcium is an important plant nutrient and is removed from the soil by crop plants. It is particularly important for brassica crops, which may remove the equivalent of 400 kg/ha of ground limestone per season.

Calcium is an essential component of plant cell walls and its deficiency thus causes poor cell development. Leaves may fail to unfold while the tissue necrosis associated with tip-burn of lettuce and internal browning of Brussels sprouts, for example, is caused either by calcium deficiency in the soil or its lack of mobility within the plants following uptake. In Britain the presence of weeds such as corn spurrey (*Spergula arvensis*), sheep's sorrel (*Rumex acetosella*) and corn marigold (*Chrysanthemum segetum*) is often an indication of acid conditions.

Vegetable crops vary in their tolerance to soil acidity but soil type, soil organic matter and rainfall can have modifying effects and it is difficult to make definite predictions. Acid conditions often cause stunting and yellowing so that growth and yield of vegetable crops on mineral soils may be reduced when pH levels fall (Table 2.2).

Table 2.2   pH levels below which crop growth may be affected

pH	Crops
7.0	Asparagus, radish
6.5	Cauliflower, spinach
6.0	Lettuce, leeks, onions, parsnips
5.5	Beans, peas, brassicas, carrots, celery
5.0	Cucumbers, marrows, tomatoes, sweet corn

In general the most favourable pH for vegetables is 6.5 in mineral soils and 6.0 in organic soils.

The availability of plant nutrients is affected considerably by the soil pH. Calcium, potassium, magnesium and sodium are alkaline elements which are lost with increasing acidity whereas phosphorus is more available in slightly acid soils although increasing acidity or highly alkaline conditions render it unavailable. Acidity can also induce deficiencies of micro-nutrients such as molybdenum, a deficiency which causes 'whiptail' (a marked reduction in leaf laminae) in cauliflower. Very acid conditions also induce deficiencies of copper and boron, although a deficiency in the latter is more commonly seen in alkaline soils where over-liming has occurred. The symptoms of boron deficiency are similar to those of calcium and include, for example, canker in beetroot, heart rot in celery and hollow or split stems in brassicas. Other minor elements which may be deficient due to low solubility at high pH values include manganese, the lack of which causes marsh spot of peas and beans, and iron, a deficiency of which produces a pale, chlorotic condition in young leaves of a number of species.

Micro-nutrient deficiencies are usually induced when the nutrients are rendered unavailable by extremes in soil reaction and are rarely caused by absence of the particular element from the soil.

The effect of liming

The incorporation of various liming materials into the soil in order to correct soil acidity results in a number of beneficial effects. For example it helps to maintain the structure of clay soils by causing the particles to aggregate into crumbs (flocculation). By affecting the activity of soil micro-organisms it also influences the rate of organic matter decomposition. Earthworms and nitrifying and nitrogen-fixing bacteria are most important and their activity is severely reduced at pHs below 5.5. Reduced bacterial action causes inefficient usage of those fertilisers and manures which require microbial conversion before they can be taken up by plants. In very acid soils the organic matter is decomposed by fungi and the resultant organic acids lead to even greater acidity.

Soil reaction can also influence the incidence of certain vegetable diseases. Club root of brassicas (*Plasmodiophora brassicae*) is more likely on acid soils while common scab of potato (*Streptomyces scabies*) is encouraged by alkaline conditions.

Liming can also influence the efficiency of soil-applied pesticides and herbicides since under acid conditions the particles adsorb the materials more strongly. Substituted urea and triazine herbicides are particularly affected, with a pH of 6.0 reducing their efficiency to half that found on well-limed soils. Similar effects have been recorded with soil-applied insecticides and nematicides.

Liming materials are frequently used to correct soil acidity but it is rarely necessary to lower pH levels, although small scale reductions can be achieved by adding sulphur to the soil.

The choice of materials for liming depends to a large extent on their relative availability and transport costs. Ground limestone or chalk ($CaCO_3$), slaked or hydrated lime ($Ca(OH)_2$), quicklime (CaO) and magnesium limestones ($CaCO_3:MgCO_3$) are the most commonly used materials. Effectiveness depends on the neutralising value (NV) of the material which indicates its ability to neutralise acid under laboratory conditions. The neutralising value is expressed in terms of calcium oxide (CaO) so that ground limestone or chalk has an NV of about 50 while slaked or hydrated lime has a value of about 70. Thus 100 kg of hydrated lime have the same neutralising value as 70 kg of calcium oxide (quicklime).

Magnesium limestones have slightly higher neutralising values than their calcium equivalents. They are particularly useful for correcting acidity on soils where magnesium deficiency may also occur. This is likely on intensively cultivated, sandy soils on which cauliflowers, potatoes or tomatoes are grown.

Materials should be applied as long as possible before sowing or planting is intended. Rain and thorough cultivation after liming will help to incorporate the materials uniformly. Lime causes premature decomposition of organic manures or fertilizers and these materials must not be mixed together. Sandy soils tend to require more frequent liming than fine-particled soils.

The exact amount of lime required can only be determined by a laboratory test. Excessive liming can induce trace element deficiencies and cause rapid organic matter decomposition. The lime requirement is the amount needed to bring mineral soils to pH 6.5 and organic soils to pH 5.8 since crop performance is similar in the two types of soil at these pH levels. Table 2.3 indicates the lime requirement of a mineral, loam soil with lime being incorporated into the top 20 cm.

Table 2.3 Approximate amounts of ground limestone required to bring the pH to 6.5

pH before liming	Quantity of ground limestone (tonnes/ha)
6.5	nil
6.0	2.5
5.5	5.0
5.0	9.0
4.5	12.5

Soil requirements for particular crops

Brassicas

Cabbage, cauliflower and Brussels sprouts are leafy crops which must grow rapidly and produce the necessary plant cover to intercept the radiation which is utilised in dry matter accumulation. Checks to growth cause slow development and inferior yields. Acid conditions must be avoided since they encourage club root disease (*Plasmodiophora brassicae*).

Where crops are direct seeded, suitable soils are required for producing seed beds which retain sufficient moisture to allow germination and sustain growth. Efficient weed control is always important but particularly for direct seeded vegetables and, since soil type influences the performance and efficiency of certain herbicides, it is vital that a suitable crop/soil/herbicide combination is chosen.

Transplanted brassicas need fertile, moisture retentive soils which allow plants to grow away rapidly.

Uniformly maturing varieties of many brassicas are now available and crops may be mechanically harvested. Poorly drained soils are never suitable since they become wet and rutted so that the passage of machines causes damage to crops and soil structure.

Legumes

Broad beans are one of the most tolerant vegetables and will grow on soils of only moderate fertility. French and runner beans, however, do best in well-drained, open-textured soils in which organic manure has been added to build up fertility and increase the moisture holding capacity. Flower drop is a serious problem in runner beans during dry conditions but is prevented by incorporating sufficient organic matter to ensure that moisture stress conditions do not develop.

Green peas are still grown for the fresh market but large quantities are also produced for processing, particularly for freezing and canning. Processors demand a programme in which crops mature successionally and this will be influenced by soil conditions. Predetermined successional sowings can only be made in soils which are always readily cultivated into a seedbed and while peas will tolerate moderately fertile soils they need adequate summer moisture if a contracted harvesting period is to be avoided.

Leeks and onions

Allium crops are sensitive to acid conditions and prefer highly fertile, moisture retentive soils. Emergence of onion and leek seedlings is slow and can be greatly reduced on silt soils which cap badly. Silty soils encourage efficient action of residual herbicides, however, and this is very important with slow growing crops of this group as they are poor natural competitors amongst weeds.

Mature onion bulbs sit on the soil surface and must not be damaged in the harvesting process otherwise they deteriorate rapidly. Consequently it is important that stony and flinty soils are not used for onions since the risk of mechanical damage is greater.

Root crops

Shallow soils are unsuitable for crops such as carrot, beetroot and parsnip while stone-free conditions are necessary to produce good quality roots. Bunching beetroot is a salad or processing crop and must be grown rapidly on fertile, moisture-retentive soils.

The more shallow-rooted globe beetroot respond to applications of farmyard manure but long beetroot, carrots and parsnips often develop poor quality fanged roots when manure is used. Carrots will not tolerate acid conditions and the harvesting of all root crops is easier from loose, friable soils.

Salad crops

Self-blanching celery and lettuce require highly fertile soils and cannot be grown efficiently and with precision without irrigation. Soils must, therefore, be able to withstand and retain regular applications of water.

Lettuce can be either transplanted or direct seeded using natural, pelleted or germinated (chitted) seed. Pelleted seed particularly requires adequate moisture to allow the pellets to split open, decompose and release the seed for germination. Lettuce will not tolerate acid conditions, especially during the seedling stages.

References and further reading

Allott, D.J. (1968) 'Experiments with contact and residual herbicides on brassica crops in Northern Irland'. *Proceedings of 9th British Weed Control Conference* British Crop Protection Council, 306–311.

Anon. (1975) 'Research and development at Wye College – a double digging machine'. *The Agricultural Engineer*, **30** (2), 36.

Haworth, F. (1965) 'Chemistry Section research report'. *Report of National Vegetable Research Station*, Wellesbourne, Warwick for 1964, 28–29.

Martin, W.P., Taylor, G.S., Engibons, J.C. and Burnett, E. (1952) 'Soil and crop responses from field applications of soil conditioners'. *Soil Science*, **73**, 455–471.

McIntyre, D.S. (1958) 'Soil splash and the formation of surface crusts by raindrop impact'. *Soil Science*, **85**, 261–266.

Menefee, E. and Hautala, E. (1978) 'Soil stabilisation by cellulose xanthate'. *Nature (Lond.)*, **275**, 530–532.

Ministry of Agriculture, Fisheries and Food (1976) *Lime in Horticulture*. Ad. Leaflet 518, London: H.M.S.O.

Ministry of Agriculture, Fisheries and Food (1968) *Soils and Manures for Vegetables*. London: H.M.S.O.

Rowse, H.R. and Stone, D.A. (1980) 'The Wye Double Digger'. *Report of National Vegetable Research Station*, Wellesbourne, Warwick for 1979, 113–114.

Russell, E.W. (1973) *Soil Conditions and Plant Growth*. 10th edn. London: Longmans.

Sale, P.J.M. and Harrison, D.J. (1964) 'Seedling emergence as affected by soil capping'. *Journal of Horticultural Science*, **39**, 147–161.

Walker, A. (1977) 'Herbicide persistance – the weather and the soil'. *A.D.A.S. Quarterly Review*, **27**, 168–179.

3　Vegetable Crop Nutrition

A number of biochemical processes are involved in plant growth. Photosynthesis is the process by which carbon dioxide and water are combined to form simple carbohydrates which are then converted into more complex sugars, starches, fats and proteins. Uptake of mineral ions through the roots provides the elements which are needed in these conversions and which are also important constituents of plant compounds such as chlorophyll. The minerals move from the roots in the water stream which spreads up through the plant to replace losses which occur through the leaves by transpiration. Respiration occurs in all living tissues and causes the biochemical breakdown of carbohydrates to release the energy needed for plant growth along with carbon dioxide and water.

The rate of growth depends on the relative rates of photosynthesis and respiration but the accumulation of dry matter will be slow unless sufficient quantities of the essential mineral nutrients are available.

Soil mineral particles of sand, silt and particularly clay weather gradually to release plant nutrients into the soil. Plant remains are decomposed by soil bacteria so that simple nitrogenous materials are eventually released. Meanwhile nutrients are lost from the soil by leaching, either by rain or irrigation, and by uptake and removal in crop plants. Burns (1974) has shown that spring and summer leaching is very important in removing nitrogenous fertilisers, particularly during the growth of crops such as lettuce, leeks and onions which provide a poor soil surface cover. Dissolved nitrogen fertilisers are a serious pollutant when they are leached down to the ground water.

The consumable portion of crops such as legumes is a relatively small part of the whole plant and crop residues which are left behind will return nutrients to the soil. However, bulky vegetables, such as cabbage, cauliflower, lettuce and spinach, remove larger quantities of nutrients from the soil thus seriously depleting reserves.

A knowledge of the nutrients which remain in, or are returned to, the soil after a particular vegetable crop allows crop rotations to be devised which utilise these residues. Nitrogen-fixing bacteria in nodules on the roots of legumes are able to build up soil nitrogen reserves for use by subsequent crops, such as cabbage, which take up large quantities of this element.

Fertilisers and manure are applied to replenish the losses described and to maintain soil fertility. Fertiliser prices are continually rising since many of the processes involved in their manufacture require considerable energy inputs. It is likely that, in time, fertilisers will be in short supply and the associated price increases will result in reductions in fertiliser use, particularly in less affluent communities. Greenwood *et al.* (1974) have stressed the need to understand more precisely the quantities required by particular crops and not to apply excessive amounts which may cause luxury uptake without increase in yield. There is also evidence in Britain, (Greenwood *et al.* 1974), that many soils which have been used regularly for vegetable crops contain luxury quantities of phosphate and potassium. Further applications cause no increase in yield and, in the case of potassium, can reduce the uptake of other nutrients such as calcium and magnesium.

Deficiencies of major crop nutrients such as nitrogen usually occur because there are insufficient reserves in the soil. The soil reaction can be important, however, as in the case of phosphate which is readily available in slighly acid conditions but unavailable at both very high or very low pHs. Micro-nutrient deficiencies are usually caused by non-availability rather than by absolute absence. Reduced calcium uptake in the presence of excessive potassium has been mentioned and similar antagonistic interactions occur when potassium reduces the uptake of magnesium; nitrate nitrogen reduces the uptake of phosphorus and calcium reduces the uptake of potassium and boron. The importance of providing a balanced supply of nutrients and maintaining the optimum soil pH cannot be over-emphasised.

Plant nutrients and their uptake

Water culture experiments have demonstrated which nutrients are needed to produce balanced growth. It is now generally accepted that nitrogen (N), phosphorus (P), potassium (K), calcium (Ca), Magnesium (Mg) and sulphur (S) are of major importance while boron (B), zinc (Zn), molybdenum (Mo), manganese (Mn), iron (Fe) and copper (Cu) are the important micro- or trace elements.

Sodium (Na) and chlorine (Cl) may also be locally important micro-elements for crops such as brassicas and beetroot. Wallace (1961) has described the effects of nutrient deficiencies on crop growth. Mineral nutrient ions may be taken up from the soil solution by plant roots and the availability of a particular ion is influenced by the amount of nutrient added to the soil, the soil pH and the cation exchange capacities (c.e.c.) of the soil constituents. Plant nutrients are released into the soil solution as positively charged cations from clay mineral and organic matter particles and are replaced by calcium ions. The c.e.c. indicates the potential of particular soil constituents for releasing cations into the soil solution and contributing to plant nutrition. Clay minerals usually have lower ratings than organic matter but both are more useful in this respect than silt or sand particles.

Nitrogen
Nitrogen is the most abundant element in the earth's atmosphere and Fig. 3.1 illustrates the pathways of the nitrogen cycle in nature.

Nitrate (NO_3^-) and ammonium (NH_4^+) ions are absorbed by plant roots, translocated to the leaves and synthesised into amino acids which are then built into complex proteins. Nitrogen is also a component of the chlorophyll pigment and deficiency causes leaf yellowing and stunted growth resulting from reduced protein synthesis. Any available nitrogen is translocated to the young leaves and the oldest leaves first exhibit deficiency symptoms. Brassicas are particularly sensitive to nitrogen deficiency and the leaves soon change from yellow to orange and then become red/purple. Nitrates are quickly washed from the soil and while the ammonium form is not leached it is rapidly converted to nitrate. Losses of nitrate are also caused by denitrification (conversion to nitrogen gas) and immobilisation (temporary reversion to unavailable organic nitrogen). Heavy textured soils retain more nitrogen than light soils. Gradual applications of nitrogenous fertilisers throughout the growing season will minimise leaching losses.

Root nodules on leguminous plants such as peas and beans contain bacteria (*Rhizobium* spp.) which are able to 'fix' atmospheric nitrogen and convert it into a form usable by plants. Soil temperatures are not always high enough to encourage sufficient *Rhizobium* activity and legumes may then respond to nitrogenous fertilisers. Artificial innoculation of seeds with *Rhizobium* in a peat mixture improves the rate of nodulation in cold soils but Hardaker and Hardwick (1978) have shown even better results by innoculating

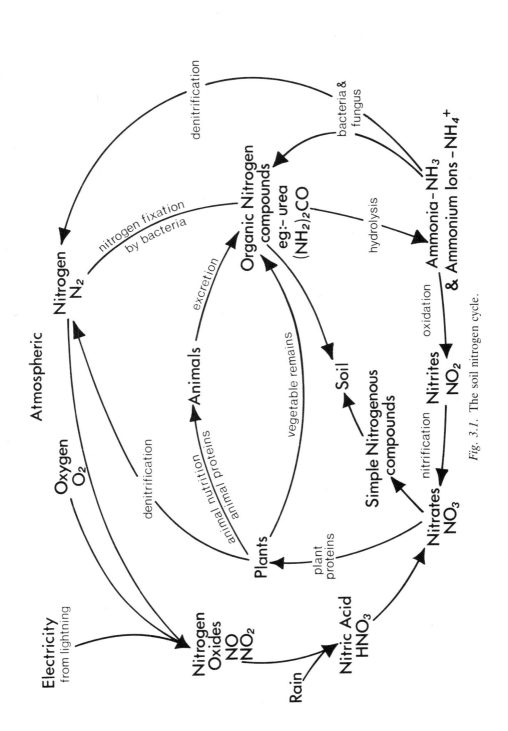

Fig. 3.1. The soil nitrogen cycle.

germinated *Phaseolus vulgaris* seed in the gel medium prior to sowing by the fluid drilling technique.

Nitrogen encourages vegetative growth but excessive amounts encourage the production of soft tissues which are easily damaged by bruising, diseases and frost. Potassium balances excess nitrogen and hardens the tissues so that cold injury is less likely on British overwintered crops such as cauliflower, cabbage and bulb onions. Excessive nitrogen delays flowering and fruiting in leguminous crops while large amounts in vegetable seedbeds cause damage to young roots and reduce seedling emergence.

Nitrogen is the most important nutrient for vegetables when rapid, uninterrupted growth is required.

Phosphorus
This element is very important in the respiration processes and also contributes to the synthesis of carbohydrates, fats and proteins. Deficiency symptoms include reduced growth and dull purple leaves (contrast with the bright purple leaves caused by severe nitrogen deficiency). High levels of phosphorus, cause a reduction in vegetative growth and also accelerate plant maturation which may result in yield reductions. Excess phosphorus can also reduce the availability of potassium and magnesium.

Phosphorus stimulates root growth particularly in the seedling stages. Availability to plants is greatly reduced in markedly acid or alkaline conditions and careful control of the pH can improve phosphate uptake.

Potassium
Some of the clay minerals are rich in potassium which is gradually released into the soil. It balances the plant against excessive nitrogen and provides increased disease resistance, cold hardiness and drought tolerance. Potassium plays a vital part in regulating water loss by transpiration, an important factor on coarse, shallow soils where drying out can occur very rapidly in warm weather.

The typical deficiency symptom is a necrotic margin around the leaf. The symptom first appears on the oldest leaves and badly affected plants are stunted.

Excess potassium can cause a reduction in magnesium and calcium uptake.

Calcium
Calcium is important in the soil from where losses are mainly caused

by leaching and crop uptake so that acid conditions develop (see chapter 2). Liming corrects acidity and provides the calcium which is essential for plant growth.

Calcium is a component of cell walls and is concerned with meristematic activity. It is relatively immobile within the plant so that deficiency symptoms usually appear first on the young tissues resulting in tip-burn of lettuce, blossom-end rot of tomatoes and internal browning of Brussels sprouts. The characteristic symptom is browning or shrivelling of the tissues.

Excessive calcium creates a high pH and can cause induced deficiencies of phosphorus and micro-nutrients such as boron, iron and manganese.

Magnesium
This element is an essential part of the chlorophyll molecule and inter-veinal chlorosis is a common deficiency symptom. Magnesium is mobile within the plant and is moved to the young leaves during periods of deficiency so that chlorosis develops first on the oldest leaves. Magnesium deficiency is shown very typically by tomatoes. Uptake is reduced by the presence of high concentrations of potassium in the soil.

Micro-nutrients
Although only small quantities of micro-nutrients are required for plant growth, deficiencies can cause severe reductions in yield and quality. Micro-nutrient deficiencies sometimes develop when the particular elements are absent from the soil but in most instances the problem arises from unsuitable soil conditions, such as pH, which render the element unavailable for crop uptake.

Table 3.1 indicates the deficiency symptoms and soil conditions associated with the common micro-nutrient deficiencies of vegetables. Further details are outlined by Mitchell (1963).

Micro-nutrient deficiencies are controlled either by correcting the pH or by adding small amounts of the appropriate chemical to the soil. Application of excessive amounts can cause reduced availability and deficiencies of other micro-nutrients and, with the exception of iron, foliar applications may be the most convenient and appropriate methods of correction (see table 3.4).

Fertiliser programmes

Experimental evidence and practical experience of vegetable crop

Table 3.1   Micro-nutrient deficiencies of vegetables

Micro-nutrient	Deficiency symptoms and conditions caused	Soil conditions influencing deficiency
Boron	Internal tissues become brown. Growing points may die. *Brown heart* of swedes; *canker* of beet-root, *cracked stem* of celery.	High pH Excessive liming Well-drained soils
Zinc	Leaf mottling Stunted growth	High pH Too much phosphate
Molybdenum	Reduced leaf lamina and stunted growth. Particularly important on brassicas e.g. *whiptail* of cauliflower.	Low pH
Manganese	Interveinal chlorosis on oldest leaves first. *Marsh spot* of peas/beans causes dark brown patches on cotyledons and young leaves.	High pH Too much organic matter Poor drainage
Iron	Interveinal chlorosis or complete yellowing/whitening of youngest leaves first.	Excessive liming Too much manganese or zinc Waterlogged or leached soils
Copper	Young onion leaves turn yellow/white. Pea/bean leaves may look grey/green.	Excessive liming Poor acid/peaty soils

nutrition have been accumulated over many years and a publication from the Ministry of Agriculture, Fisheries and Food (1968) gives general indications of the amounts of major nutrients that individual crops may remove from different soils under British conditions. Most of the data on fertiliser programmes have come from conventional randomised block field experiments which need large areas of land and require considerable numbers of guard plants. Cleaver *et al.* (1970) showed the value of more compact experimental layouts with systematic designs. The results hvae been used in comparative studies of major crop nutrient responses on a wide range of vegetables (Greenwood *et al.*, 1974).

The majority of vegetable fertiliser programmes are still formulated after a combined assessment of (1) previous cropping on the site, (2) crop appearance and performance and (3) laboratory analyses of soil or plant material. Soil and plant analytical techniques have been described by Ministry of Agriculture, Fisheries and Food (1973).

Soil analysis

Soil analytical services are usually available from government and commercial advisory organisations. Regular soil analyses are used to indicate (1) the initial (base dressing) or total fertiliser requirement for particular crops, (2) the rate of accumulation or depletion of nutrients and (3) the causes of nutritional problems. Vegetable growing soils should be checked at the beginning of each season and also between crops if heavy rainfall, frequent irrigation or crop problems have occurred. Soil samples can be taken by the advisory officer or the farmer but must be representative of the area in question. Sampling techniques vary and the instructions must be followed precisely. Soil should always be collected in clean containers and carefully labelled.

Most soil analytical services are able to provide information on soil pH; lime requirement; available phosphorus, potassium and magnesium levels; percentage organic matter; total nitrogen content; trace element levels and electrical conductivity (a measure of the total soluble salt concentration). There are no satisfactory analytical methods for determining the amount of nitrogen in a soil sample that is immediately available for plant growth. The percentage organic matter and total nitrogen content give indications of overall soil fertility and this can be a useful guide to nitrogen availability. A knowledge of previous cropping and manurial history of the site is also used when assessing nitrogen requirements. Interpretation of analytical results requires considerable skill and experience but most advisory services will provide recommendations for specific crops.

The British agricultural advisory service (A.D.A.S.) uses an index system to express soil nutrient levels. Indices range from 0–9 with high numbers indicating greater quantities of available nutrient. Vegetable soils often have indices of 2 or 3 for phosphorus and potassium and a magnesium index of 1. Tables are used to convert indices to quantities of nutrients required by individual crops (Ministry of Agriculture, Fisheries and Food, 1979). The general relationship between indices and soil nutrient status is shown in table 3.2

Table 3.2 A.D.A.S. Indices and soil nutrient status for vegetables

Index	Nutrient status
0	Deficient
1	Low – extra fertiliser required
2–3	Normal – fertiliser programmes for individual crops based on these average figures
4–5	Above normal – P and K dressings may be reduced
6–8	Very high – no fertiliser needed
9	Excessive – growth will be depressed

Soil analysis has some drawbacks as a means of monitoring crop nutrition. There may, for example, be considerable delay between sampling and receipt of the results and while regular soil analyses provide useful indications of medium and long term variations they are less useful for monitoring any short term changes. Soil analysis results are a useful guide but must be studied in conjunction with many interacting factors including previous cropping, soil type and depth, plant spacing and soil moisture. Soil nutrient analyses do not necessarily indicate the amounts taken up by plants and it is possible for deficiencies to occur even when sufficient nutrients are recorded as being present in the soil.

Visual assessments of crop performance are very important and in conjunction with plant analyses, will provide information on nutrient uptake.

Leaf analysis

Leaf analysis provides a direct measurement of nutrient content with the quantity of each nutrient being expressed as a percentage of the total plant dry matter. Accurate and representative sampling is again important but regular determination can be used to monitor nutrient uptake throughout the life of a crop. Major and micro-nutrients can be measured but laboratory procedures are often time-consuming and expensive. Interpretation of data may also be difficult particularly when there are delays between sampling and obtaining the results. Direct analysis techniques for use in the field would be valuable to both farmers and advisors and regular monitoring would enable problems to be foreseen and remedied quickly. Tests for the extraction and analysis of plant sap have been described by Scaife and Bray (1977) in which nutrient concentrations are indicated colorimetrically on simple plastic strips. Such sap tests are particularly useful for nitrogen determinations but potassium and calcium can also be checked in a similar way. Analysis of sap from leaves on different parts of the plant allows mobile (N, P, K, Mg) and immobile (Ca, B, Fe) elements to be monitored.

Comparative studies

Greenwood *et al.* (1974), in Britain, compared the responsiveness of a wide range of vegetables to nitrogen, phosphorus and potassium with the performance of agricultural crops which were grown in nationwide fertiliser experiments. Yield responses were then predicted for applications of various amounts of N, P and K to vegetables on a range of soil types. Comparison of the predictions with actual results showed very close similarities for both phosphorus and potassium although responses to nitrogen were less predictable. Further studies in conjunction with surveys carried out by the national advisory service (ADAS) have demonstrated luxury levels of phosphorus and potassium in many soils which have been regularly cropped with vegetables.

On the basis of these studies an NPK response predictor for use on a wide range of vegetables was first published in 1975 and has since been further improved in the light of more recent experience (National Vegetable Research Station, 1980a). Part of the problem in predicting responses to nitrogen applications derives from the occurrence of leaching although, at least on certain soils, it is possible to estimate such losses using a simple calculator developed at the National Vegetable Research Station (1980b). By using such predictors, a grower is able to assess the nutritional requirements of his crops more precisely and reduce costs through eliminating wasteful applications of fertilisers. It is also likely that the use of mechanistic models of crop responses to fertiliser application, in conjunction with the increasing availability of microcomputers, will play an important role in the future formulation of efficient and economic fertiliser programmes (Greenwood, 1983).

Calculation of fertiliser application rates

Recommendations on fertiliser requirements based on the methods outlined above may take a number of forms. They can for example be stated in terms of the element alone (i.e. NPK, etc.) although in Britain and many other countries recommended rates of application, with the exclusion of nitrogen, are more frequently based on their oxides. For example, phosphorus is expressed as phosphorus pentoxide (P_2O_5) and potassium as potassium oxide (K_2O). The use of these terms, which derive largely from early analytical techniques, is unfortunate and can lead to some confusion. In fact one of the more common sources of potassium is potassium chloride (KCl) which contains no oxygen.

Before metrication, fertiliser recommendations were frequently expressed in 'units' of nitrogen (N), phosphate (P_2O_5) or potash (K_2O) where a unit was defined as 1% of the old Imperial 'hundredweight'. Rates are now more correctly expressed in kilograms per hectare (1 unit per acre being equivalent to approximately 1.25 kilograms per hectare). The rate of application of any nutrient can be readily calculated from a knowledge of its percentage present in a given fertiliser. For example, if analysis indicates that a crop requires 60 kg/ha of nitrogen (N) and the nitrogenous fertiliser available contains 30% nitrogen (N) then 200 kg/ha of the fertiliser would be needed to supply the recommended amount of nitrogen. Alternative sources of nitrogen and other nutrients will be covered in more detail later in the chapter.

Timing of applications

Nitrate nitrogen is rapidly leached from soils and the timing of fertiliser applications must be carefully adjusted to ensure that sufficient nutrient is always available in the soil. Leaching losses of phosphatic and potassic fertilisers are insignificant. Fertilisers may be applied as base dressings before establishing the crop and, at a later stage as top dressings. Base dressing fertiliser treatments, applied and incorporated before crops are sown or planted, are usually one of the final operations before tilth preparation. Applications made too far in advance of crop establishment can result in wasteful leaching losses.

The electrical conductivity (soluble salt concentration) of the soil solution is increased by dissolved fertilisers, particularly those containing nitrates and chlorides. As the ion concentration increases there are corresponding increases in osmotic potential which can slow down and eventually prevent imbibition of water by seeds and young seedlings. The germination and seedling emergence of vegetables can be severely reduced following high pre-sowing applications of nitrogenous fertilisers – lettuce, carrots and onions being particularly sensitive in this respect. Greenwood (1972) has shown that rainfall immediately following sowing increases the seed tolerance to this form of damage, presumably as a consequence of diluting salt concentrations and regular irrigation applications could be expected to achieve a similar effect.

In spite of the disadvantages associated with premature or excessive pre-sowing applications of fertilisers, if all nutrients could be provided as a single base dressing there would be considerable savings in application costs and reduced crop damage from machinery used for fertiliser distribution. There are only minor phytotoxicity dangers associated with phosphatic and potassic fertilisers and all their requirements can be applied before sowing with little risk of damage.

Application of a crop's fertiliser requirement in a single treatment before sowing is particulrly favoured by large, farm-scale vegetable producers and in such instances some of the seedling emergence problems may be avoided by using banded applications in which the fertiliser is placed at a safe distance from the future location of the germinating seed. Transplanted and established vegetables are less susceptible to fertiliser injury but some growth reductions may still occur. Although it is common practice to apply all the phosphate and potash as a base dressing there are often gains to be made by withholding part of the nitrogen for applying as one or more top dressings later during the crop's development. This helps to overcome any potential seedling emergence problem as a result of high salt concentration and also ensures that regular supplies of nitrogen are available throughout crop growth. Top dressings are given to sustain rapid growth and the materials must be quick acting. Less fertiliser is wasted since leaching losses are reduced but heavy rainfall or irrigation will quickly deplete soil nitrogen reserves and further applications are soon needed if deficiencies are to be avoided. Top dressings should ideally be given in showery conditions but if this is not possible, irrigation can be used immediately after fertiliser application to wash the nutrients into the root zone. Foliar applications of fertiliser or liquid feeding through the irrigation water overcome the problems of top dressing in dry weather.

Top dressing at regular intervals optimises the use of fertilisers, especially with long season crops such as Brussels sprouts and cauliflower, but there may be problems of machinery access when the plants are closely spaced and have formed a complete leaf canopy. Crop damage and poor fertiliser distribution will reduce yield but the problems are reduced when vegetables are grown in beds which can be straddled by machinery. Aerial applications are an alternative but field size and poor penetration of fertiliser into the crop can cause difficulties.

Application procedures

Solid fertilisers for vegetables are either applied by broadcasting them on the soil and/or crop, or by placing them in bands on or in the soil. Broadcasting is relatively easy and most mechanical fertiliser distributors utilise this technique. Broadcast base dressing fertilisers are usually incorporated into the surface layers of the soil prior to sowing or planting but better growth and higher yields result from incorporating the nutrients throughout the entire cultivated depth.

Broadcasting top dressing materials over growing crops can cause damage if corrosive fertilisers lodge in or on soft plant tissues. Developing cauliflower curds are easily damaged and sweet corn can be stunted if nitrogenous fertiliser granules fall within the terminal, protective leaf sheaths and burn the growing point.

Wastage and crop damage are drawbacks to broadcasting which may be overcome by fertiliser placement. Phosphatic fertilisers are very important for early root growth and seedling development but they are quickly converted into compounds from which plants cannot obtain the phosphate. Broadcasting means that fertiliser which falls away from the root zone will never be available. A band of phosphatic fertiliser placed 5 cm to the side and below the seed provides a better supply of nutrients with less wastage. This more efficient use of fertiliser may make it possible to reduce the quantity applied compared with a broadcast application.

The potential yield advantages from fertiliser placement compared with broadcasting are illustrated for a number of leguminous crops in table 3.3.

The usual application rates of phosphatic fertilisers will not cause increases in the soil salt concentration and reduce seedling emergence. Close placement of fertilisers which release nitrate or chloride ions will cause emergence problems but it is possible to band the materials between the rows where young roots are less likely to reach the high salt concentrations.

Placement of top dressing materials (side dressing) also makes more efficient use of fertilisers by putting the nutrients near to the

Table 3.3 Comparison of fertiliser placement and broadcasting on leguminous crops

	Fertiliser analysis			Fertiliser rate (kg/ha)	Crop Yield (kg/ha)		
Crop	%N	%P$_2$O$_5$	%K$_2$O		No Fertiliser	Broadcast	Placed
Broad beans	7.0	7.0	10.5	627	8 030	8 270	9 530
Runner beans	7.0	7.0	10.5	627	12 170	13 170	14 050
Green peas	0	13	13	749	9 030	9 530	10 910
Dried peas	0	10	20	749	1 720	1 860	2 060

(After Ignatieff and Page, 1958)

site of absorption and minimising the risk of chemical damage to crops.

Fertiliser formulation

The majority of solid fertilisers are formulated into granules which readily roll off crop plants. Granules are usually more or less spherical but some fertilisers, for example sulphate of ammonia ($(NH_4)_2SO_4$), consist of small, crystalline particles while others such as superphosphate of lime are available as fine powders. Compound fertilisers containing a mixture of different compounds are usually formulated as granules. Crystalline or powdered formulations are more likely to remain on crops and cause scorching and should therefore be distributed at low level and preferably followed by an immediate application of water to wash any traces of fertiliser from the crop leaves into the root zone.

Nutrients may also be applied in a solution which may be injected into the soil or applied through the irrigation system. Plants are capable of absorbing the majority of mineral nutrients through the leaves and although foliar feeding is rarely the most economic method of supplying all the major nutrient requirements it can be particularly useful in dry soil areas and for obtaining rapid correction of micro-nutrient and other deficiencies. Examples of foliar sprays for correcting nutrient and other deficiencies are shown in table 3.4 but care is necessary since plants usually need very small quantities and excesses can cause phytotoxicity and growth depression.

Complete foliar feeding involves the application of specially formulated solutions which often contain a surfactant to encourage

Table 3.4 Foliar sprays for correcting nutrient deficiencies

Deficient element	Chemical to be sprayed	Weight to be dissolved and sprayed in 250–1000 litres per ha (kg)
Magnesium	Magnesium sulphate (Epsom salts)	22.40
Boron	Sodium borate (Borax)	5.60
Manganese	Manganese sulphate	4.50–9.00
Molybdenum	Sodium molybdate	0.28
Zinc	Zinc sulphate	0.56

even wetting of the leaves. Application is by conventional spraying machines but great care is needed to ensure that mixtures with other agricultural chemicals (e.g. crop protection materials) are compatible and non-phytotoxic.

Application of top dressing fertilisers in irrigation water (liquid feeding) has many advantages in dry climates but there are problems when crops need top dressing and irrigation is not required.

Rain may wash off the nutrients before they have been absorbed but they may then be taken up by the plant roots. Solutions of water soluble nitrogenous fertilisers, such as urea, may evaporate and leave corrosive fertiliser deposits on soft tissues. Crop damage and unsightly fertiliser deposits are avoided by irrigating with clear water after liquid feeding.

In summary, there are many techniques of applying nutrients for crop growth and the following are all possible depending on the circumstances:

- Broadcasting or placement by hand.
- Broadcasting or placement by fertiliser distributor, seed drill or transplanter.
- Overall application via sprinkler, or other overhead irrigation system.
- Placement by ground level drip or trickle irrigation system.
- Soil injection.
- By air.

Broadcasting techniques are more usual but overhead and ground level irrigation systems are increasingly used in tropical climates.

Types of fertiliser

Fertilisers and manures are often discussed together but confusion can exist and it is more convenient to consider them as having largely different functions. Manures were discussed in chapter 2 and although they provide some essential plant nutrients the amounts and rate of release vary with the type and condition of manure. Their contribution to the overall nutritional programme should not be ignored but it is difficult to calculate accurately and they are best regarded as soil conditioning agents which make long term improvements to the fertility, functioning and environment of the growing medium. These improvements help the plants to make more efficient use of the fertilisers which are used to supply the specific nutrient requirements of individual crops. The combined use and interaction of (a) bulky manures, (b) fertilisers and (c) liming materials is essential in maintaining the high levels of soil fertility required for successful vegetable growing. Failure to optimise any one of the three factors will lead to inefficient use of the other two.

Fertilisers may be derived from either organic or inorganic materials and they may be simple (straight) or compound. Simple fertilisers supply only one of the three major plant nutrients e.g. sulphate of ammonia (N); superphosphate of lime (P_2O_5) and sulphate of potash (K_2O). Compound fertilisers contain two or more of the major plant nutrients in a range of different proportions. Compounds applied as base dressings represent the majority of fertilisers used for commercial vegetable production but simple fertilisers are used to make up individual nutrients to prescribed levels and to provide top dressing nitrogen.

It is very convenient to buy ready-formulated compounds but ones with the required nutrient ratio may not be available and on the farm mixing of simple fertilisers may be necessary to produce the exact combination.

Compound fertilisers are usually granular and easy to handle. They are more expensive than the combination of simple fertilisers which would be necessary to provide the same plant nutrients. Compounds rarely meet the exact requirements of any crops and a grower who produces a large range of vegetables could need many different compounds.

In Britain E.E.C. regulations govern the declaration of nutrients present in compound fertilisers (Ministry of Agriculture, Fisheries and Food, 1978). A compound fertiliser, for example, may be designated 20:10:10 which means that it contains 20% N : 10% total P_2O_5 : 10% K_2O. In this case 100 kg of the compound provide 20 kg N, 10 kg P_2O_5 and 10 kg K_2O, but if a vegetable crop requires a base fertiliser dressing of 80 kg N, 60 kg P_2O_5 and 120 kg K_2O then 400 kg of the compound in question will provide 80 kg N but only 40 kg P_2O_5 and 40 kg K_2O. The remaining 20 kg P_2O_5 and 80 kg K_2O must then be provided by appropriate quantities of simple fertilisers.

Nitrogenous fertilisers

Nitrogenous fertilisers are either organic or inorganic in origin. Organic fertilisers are derived from living material and usually contain less nitrogen than inorganic ('artificial') materials. Nitrogen from organic materials is often released more slowly than from inorganic sources and crops therefore receive a steady supply throughout the growing period. Organic fertilisers will not however encourage sustained, rapid growth and are of little use on quickly maturing crops. Dangers of reduced seedling emergence and plant scorch may be less than with inorganic fertilisers but this will depend on the particle sizes since finely ground organics will release nitrogen and cause damage very quickly.

The unit cost of nutrients is much greater from organic fertilisers and, although the materials are of biological origin they do not improve soil structural conditions or enhance crop quality anymore than inorganic materials.

Table 3.5 Organic nitrogenous fertilisers

Fertiliser	Nutrient percentage	Comments
Hoof and horn	13% N	Slow release of N Fine particles release N faster than coarse material
Dried blood	10–13%	Quick acting (as rapid as inorganic fertiliser) Partly or completely water soluble
Meat and bone meal	Approximately 7% N 16% P_2O_5	Percentage of N varies and falls as the amount of bone increases
Shoddy	Up to 12–15% N	Waste from woollen mills Pure wool gives highest % N

Table 3.6   Inorganic nitrogenous fertilisers

Fertiliser	Nutrient percentage	Comments
Ammonium nitrate (NH_4NO_3)	33.5–34.5% N	Half N as NO_3^- (immediately available) and half as NH_4^+ (slowly released) Acidifies the soil Store away from inflammable materials
Sulphate of ammonia ($(NH_4)_2SO_4$)	21% N	Acidifies the soil NH_4^+ nitrogen must be converted to NO_3 Crystals may lodge on plants and cause scorching
Urea ($(NH_2)_2CO$)	45%	Converted into NH_4^+ nitrogen in soil Dangerous when applied near to germinating seeds N easily lost from alkaline and sandy soils in dry conditions
Chilean Potash nitrate ($NaNO_3:KNO_3$)	15% N 10% K_2O 10–18% Na	Useful mixture of nutrients Popular use as top dressing on intensive vegetables
Potassium nitrate (KNO_3)	12–14% N 44% K_2O	Used for glasshouse and intensive vegetable crops
Anhydrous ammonia (NH_3)	82% N	Must be kept under high pressure Needs strict safety precautions and efficient injection Similar action to ammonium fertilisers Severe leaching losses in wet soil conditions Ammonia damage most likely in sandy soils
Aqueous ammonia (NH_4OH)	21–29%	Similar to anhydrous ammonia Kept under lower pressures than anhydrous form Needs injecting but losses are less than with anhydrous ammonia Seedling damage less than with ammonium nitrate or anhydrous ammonia

Inorganic nitrogenous fertilisers are very soluble in water and release nitrogen quickly in a form which crops can use. They are readily leached from porous, well-drained soils and can cause problems as pollutants of ground water. The properties of some of the more commonly used organic and inorganic nitrogenous fertilisers are shown in tables 3.5 and 3.6 respectively.

Phosphatic fertilisers

Phosphate can be added to the soil as either water soluble (e.g. superphosphate) or insoluble (e.g. bone meal) fertilisers. Water soluble phosphate is immediately available to plants but soil conditions – particularly pH – greatly influence long term availability. Insoluble forms release their phosphate very slowly. Phosphate is most available to crops in soils with values of pH 6.0–6.5, which is one of the reasons why this slightly acid range is favoured for vegetable crop production. At low pH values (below 5.5) the phosphate is converted to insoluble iron and aluminium phosphates while insoluble calcium phosphates are formed in very alkaline conditions (above pH 7.5). Phosphate fixation in average soils renders 70–75% of recently applied water soluble phosphate unavailable to the next crop and recovery rates can be very low indeed on some soils. Fixed phosphate only becomes slowly available again over a period of years.

Seedlings benefit from phosphate at an early stage and rapid uptake is enhanced by placement of soluble materials in bands close to the plants. Application should be as close as possible to sowing or planting time so that fixation losses are reduced.

British soils which have been cropped with vegetables for several years often contain considerable phosphate reserves and further applications do not produce growth or yield increases.

The properties of commonly used phosphatic fertilisers are shown in table 3.7.

Table 3.7 Phosphatic fertilisers

Fertiliser	Nutrient percentage	Comments
Superphosphate ($Ca(H_2PO_4)_2 + CaSO_4$)	18–20% water soluble P_2O_5	Powdered and granular forms Short-term and long-term action
Triple superphosphate ($Ca(H_2PO_4)_2$)	47% water soluble P_2O_5	
Ground mineral phosphate	25–40% total P_2O_5	Fine grinding increases nutrient availability Most efficient in high rainfall areas Poor efficiency for continuous vegetable cropping where pH is above 6.5
Bone meal	22% total P_2O_5; 2–5% N	Fine grinding increases nutrient availability
Steamed bone flour	28% total P_2O_5; 1% N	Used for glasshouse and intensive vegetable crops

Potassic fertilisers

Leaching of potassium rarely occurs and fertilisers can be applied long before crop establishment. Plants may continue to take up potassium even though there are no further yield increases (luxury uptake) and brassicas, cabbage and cauliflower in particular can remove large amounts of potassium from the soil, resulting in severe depletion.

Table 3.8 shows the properties of some important potassic fertilisers.

Table 3.8 Potassic fertilisers

Fertiliser	Nutrient percentage	Comments
Muriate of potash (KCl)	60% K_2O	Crystalline and granular forms available Chloride ions may cause seedling damage on sensitive crops e.g. tomatoes Hygroscopic
Sulphate of potash (K_2SO_4)	50% K_2O	Safer than muriate but more expensive Less hygroscopic
Potassium nitrate (KNO_3)	44% K_2O 12–14% N	Useful in liquid feeds and for intensive production systems

Nutrition of particular vegetables

Specific fertiliser requirements depend on many factors, the relative importance of which may vary in different parts of the world. It is possible, however, to make general comments about the requirements of groups of crops.

Leafy and heading brassicas

This groups includes the cabbages, Brussels sprouts, cauliflower and various kinds of broccoli. Vegetative growth is important but cold tolerance may also be necessary for some crops grown in temperate climates. Nitrogen is the most important nutrient when there is no danger of low temperature injury. Nutrient uptake is improved by regular irrigation in dry climates when regular top dressings with nitrogen fertilisers will avoid excessive leaching losses. Applications of large amounts of nitrogen in warm, well irrigated soils will produce soft growth which is susceptible to disease and mechanical injury.

Brassicas which are grown through cold winter conditions require sufficient potassic fertiliser to balance any soft vegetative growth. Crops which continue to grow and then are harvested some time after the winter will require top dressings of nitrogen when regrowth begins.

Cabbage for winter storage will be harvested before the onset of severe weather but they must not be grown with too much nitrogen or they will be soft, liable to harvesting damage and store badly.

Legumes

Nitrogen-fixing bacteria (*Rhizobium spp.*) are found in nodules on the roots of legumes. When they are functioning efficiently it may be unnecessary to apply much nitrogenous fertiliser. Excessive nitrogen will cause too much vegetative growth and reduce pod formation. Lush vegetative growth also favours fungal or bacterial diseases and reduces the efficiency of mechanical harvesting.

Peas have a low nitrogen requirement and it can be omitted on all but the most infertile soils or after prolonged periods of nutrient leaching. Broad beans also do well on moderately fertile soils but overwintered crops must be sown into a low-nitrogen seedbed and top-dressed when growth recommences.

Runner and French beans grow best in fertile, moisture-retentive soils. Nitrogen top dressings and irrigation may improve the appearance, succulence and quality of the pods for which these crops are usually grown.

Leeks and onions

Bulb onions need nitrogen to build up a vegetative framework of leaves but too much nitrogen during bulbing promotes soft growth which is easily damaged and the bulbs do not store well. Crops which are grown through cold winter conditions as young plants must not be given too much nitrogen until the return of higher temperatures which promote further growth.

Bunching onions have similar nutritional requirements but close spacings are used to increase inter-plant competition and reduce bulb size.

Leeks must produce a considerable amount of vegetative growth and nitrogenous fertilisers are very important. They are commonly grown as a winter vegetable, when the nitrogen must be balanced with potash to prevent too much soft, lush growth.

Root crops

Phosphates are usually required for root development but easily cultivated soils are equally important. Crops which are produced for rapidly grown, crisp and succulent roots (e.g. bunching beetroot and early turnips) are very dependent upon supplies of nitrogenous fertiliser.

Roots which are produced for winter harvesting or storage must not be too soft or they will rot in the ground or in store.

Fresh animal manure causes carrot and other roots to fork (fanging) when it remains in the surface layers of the soil.

Salads and other crops

Salads are usually short-term crops which are grown intensively. They must grow rapidly and irrigation is an important production aid. Reasonable supplies of nitrogen are needed to produce the vegetative growth of lettuce but excessive amounts in the seedbed must be avoided. Radishes need nitrogen and uninterrupted supplies of moisture to produce crisp, solid roots. The same conditions are necessary for self-blanching celery but winter-maturing celery requires high levels of potassium to prevent cold injury.

Tomatoes should be given a balanced fertiliser since nitrogen is needed to promote vegetative growth while potassium influences fruit production and quality. Cucurbitous crops (marrows, courgettes, melons, gourds, etc.) grow very rapidly in fertile, well-manured soils but nitrogen may be needed in the early stages if growth is slow. Too much nitrogen encourages excessive leafiness which can deter fruiting and make harvesting more difficult.

Steady and regular supplies of nitrogen and moisture are needed to produce a strong and vigorous plant framework for sweet corn. Sufficient leaf area is also needed to assimilate the carbohydrates which are necessary for rapid and uniform cob formation.

References and further reading

Burns, I.G. (1974) 'A model for predicting the redistribution of salts applied to fallow soils after excess rainfall or evaporation'. *Journal of Soil Science*, **25**, 165–178.

Cleaver, T.J., Greenwood, D.J. and Wood, J.T. (1970) 'Systematically arranged fertiliser experiments'. *Journal of Horticultural Science*, **45**, 457–469.

Cooke, G.W. (1982) *Fertilising for Maximum Yield*. 3rd edn. London: Granada Publishing.

Greenwood, D.J. (1972) 'Inter-year variability in the effects of nitrogen fertiliser on the stand of lettuce'. *Report of National Vegetable Research Station*, Wellesbourne, Warwick for 1971, 34.

Greenwood, D.J. (1983) 'Quantitative theory and the control of soil fertility'. *New Phytologist*, **94**, 1–18.

Greenwood, D.J., Cleaver, T.J. and Turner, M.K. (1974) 'Fertiliser requirements of vegetable crops'. *Proceedings of Fertiliser Society*, **145**, 1–30.

Hardaker, J.M. and Hardwick, R.C. (1978) 'A note on *Rhizobium* inoculation of beans (*Phaseolus vulgaris*) using the fluid drill technique'. *Experimental Agriculture*, **14**, 17–21.

Ignatieff, V. and Page, H.J. eds. (1958) 'Efficient use of fertilisers'. *Agricultural Studies*, **43**, Rome: F.A.O.

Ministry of Agriculture, Fisheries and Food (1968) *Soils and Manures for Vegetables*. Bulletin 71. London: H.M.S.O.

Ministry of Agriculture, Fisheries and Food (1973) *Analysis of Agricultural Materials*. Technical Bulletin 27. London: H.M.S.O.

Ministry of Agriculture, Fisheries and Food (1978) *Guide to Current Fertiliser Regulations*. Leaflet AF 53. London: H.M.S.O.

Ministry of Agriculture, Fisheries and Food (1979) *Fertiliser Recommendations for Agricultural and Horticultural Crops*. Ref. G.F.1. London: H.M.S.O.

Mitchell, R.L. (1963) 'Soil aspects of trace element problems in plants and animals'. *Journal Royal Agricultural Society*, **124**, 75–86.

National Vegetable Research Station (1980a) *New NPK Predictor*, Wellesbourne, Warwick.

National Vegetable Research Station (1980b) *Nitrogen Calculator*, Wellesbourne, Warwick.

Scaife, M.A. and Bray, B.G. (1977) 'Quick sap tests for improved control of crop nutrient status'. *A.D.A.S. Quarterly Review*, **27**, 137–145.

Wallace, T. (1961) *The Diagnosis of Mineral Deficiencies in Plants by Visual Symptoms*. London: H.M.S.O.

4 Population studies and propagation methods

Introduction

The world-wide demand for vegetables continues to rise but economic, political and other pressures often make it difficult for growers to retain and maintain existing production sites. Domestic and industrial buildings spread onto areas around towns and cities, labour drifts away from the land and soil fertility is increasingly difficult to maintain as supplies of organic manures dwindle. Vegetable growers are, therefore, increasingly concerned with maximising yield per unit area.

Plant populations and spacings have a great influence on yield but their effects are conditioned by other factors which can limit crop growth. Consequently growers can reduce plant populations from the optimum so that crops may be grown successfully in parts of the world with water shortage, poor soil fertility or limited fertiliser use. Population also affects individual plant size and the time taken to reach maturity and thus market requirements influence the density at which crops are grown.

A great deal of research into the effects of vegetable plant population and arrangement on yield has been carried out under temperate conditions in Britain since the mid 1950s and, while the underlying principles are universally applicable, local investigations are necessary to relate them to different crops and climates. Bleasdale (1973a) has reviewed the growing systems used for commercial vegetable crops in Britain during the last 250 years. Production in the eighteenth century relied heavily on hand labour as crops were broadcast-sown on beds and subsequently thinned, weeded and harvested by hand. Tradition and experience determined the amount of space allocated to each crop plant. Workers began to move away from the land as a result of the Industrial Revolution and were replaced by machines. Seed drills and hoes were introduced and broadcasting was replaced by row cropping systems. Hand- and horse-drawn equipment was superseded by tractor-powered machinery and the row spacings were determined by tradition and access. Wide spaces were needed for the passage of inter-row hoeing equipment. Plant spacings within the rows were also traditionally determined and the non-sophisticated drilling equipment usually produced irregular distributions. Mechanical weed control within the rows was impossible unless crops were thinned or gapped in which case weeds were removed along with unwanted crop seedlings. More recently mechanical weed control has, at least in part, been replaced by the development of sophisticated selective herbicides and it has become possible to consider closer row spacings and optimum plant populations.

The present chapter considers the theoretical background and the implications of varying plant populations and spacing, before reviewing the various techniques of propagating vegetables. The more practical aspects of establishing the appropriate populations in the field are dealt with in the following chapter.

Vegetable plant populations

Population research has been mainly concerned with plant growth and yield and while most of the work has been with seeded crops, transplanted vegetables such as potatoes (Bleasdale, 1965); closely spaced or 'mini' cauliflowers (Salter, 1971) and shallots (Warne, 1951) have also been studied.

Research has been concerned with plant populations (i.e. the number of plants per unit area) and with plant arrangement (i.e. the pattern in which the recommended number of plants is arranged). Population studies must include a wide range of treatments and field experiments using conventional randomised block designs require large amounts of land which may not be readily available. Nelder (1962) and Bleasdale (1967) devised systematic experimental designs which incorporated variations of plant populations and arrangements. The Wellesbourne 'fan design' for example provides for a range of spacings arranged on an almost square configuration. Other designs make provision for variations in the ratio between inter-row and within-row spacing (i.e. rectangularity) enabling a wide range of spacings to be tested in a small area.

Population and yield

Two basic population:yield relationships have been observed with

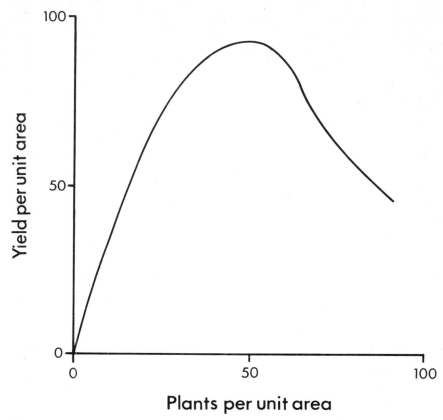

Fig. 4.1. Relationship between plant population and yield showing yield depression at high populations (after Bleasdale, 1973a).

vegetable crops. Beetroot was shown by Frappell (1968) to have the relationship shown in fig. 4.1. Yield per unit area increases with population until a certain point, beyond which further population increases cause yield reductions. Individual plant size decreases steadily as the population rises. At the point of maximum yield, plant size is only half that produced at the widest spacing (lowest population). When individual plant size is maximised the yield per unit area is less than 50% of the optimum.

Whereas beetroot yields fall sharply above the optimum population, many vegetable species show very little decrease in yield once their 'ceiling' level has been reached. In these instances the yield versus population relationship is similar to that indicated in fig. 4.2. This form of response is typified by the results of studies on carrots, but also applies to bulb onions (Bleasdale, 1966), parsnips

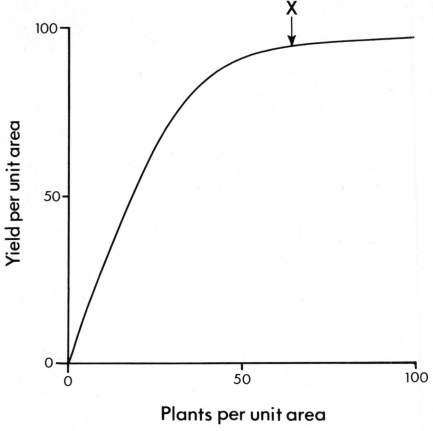

Fig. 4.2. Relationship between plant population and yield showing constant yield at high populations (after Bleasdale, 1973a).

(Bleasdale and Thompson, 1966), runner beans (Bleasdale, 1968) as well as transplanted crops such as cabbage, Brussels sprouts, calabrese (broccoli) and leeks.

Population and plant size

Root size in carrots decreases as population increases but, above a particular point (X on fig. 4.2) there is no loss of yield and by manipulating plant population the grower can thus produce roots of a particular size to meet the requirements of specific market outlets. Bleasdale's work on carrots forms a basis for the bed-system of growing this crop (Ministry of Agriculture, Fisheries and Food, 1969). Such control should, theoretically, produce a very high proportion of the roots in a pre-determined size range. Unfortunately there is often a high percentage of roots outside the specified size and this variation can be partially attributed to uneven seedling emergence (Currah, 1975).

Cauliflowers too can be grown at very close spacings (approximately 40 per m^2) when they will produce mini-curds which are ideal for processing or for pre-packed sales through supermarkets (Salter, 1971).

Similar effects are shown by bulb onions (Bleasdale, 1966) when close spacings are used to produce pickling onions and lower populations (approximately 76 per m^2 for Rijnsburger types) for ware crop production. This ware crop density often produces less (25% less with Rijnsburger types) than the maximum total yield obtained at great densities, and it would be better if the maximum ware yield occurred at the same density.

In row cropping, plants are typically established with a larger distance between rows than within rows. The ratio of the distance between rows and the average within row spacing is known as the rectangularity and an arrangement which gives plants the same amount of space in each direction gives a rectangularity ratio of 1:1. Rectangularity must be considered in conjunction with plant population as an even distribution of plants is more likely to allow equal utilisation of soil and aerial resources and to minimise competition. Figure 4.3 illustrates the degree of competition likely to develop in a row crop situation relative to that in a uniformly spaced crop at the equivalent overall population. Even spacing should allow uniform development, reduce crop and resource wastage and increase the feasibility of mechanical harvesting. Evenly spaced crops established from uniformly size-graded transplants can produce these effects but direct seeding is a more usual method of vegetable plant establishment. Seeds must be drilled at the requisite spacing but they must also germinate and emerge evenly. Gray (1976) has demonstrated the effect of emergence variation on the final yield of lettuce. Seed treatments to improve emergence and accuracy of spacing are discussed later in the chapter.

Population and crop maturity

The effects of competition between individual crop plants, and also between crop plants and weeds, are varied and in addition to their

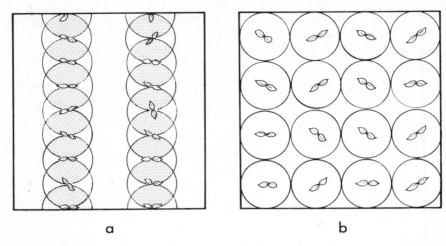

a   b

Fig. 4.3. Effect of plant arrangement on competition (a) for row crop and (b) for uniform spacing. Shaded regions represent severe competition (after Bleasdale, 1973b).

effects on size and yield can also influence the time to maturity. Cauliflowers grown at conventional spacings tend not to mature uniformly and must be selectively harvested several times by hand to produce an economic percentage cut. Salter (1971) showed that mini-cauliflowers grown at very close spacings mature earlier than conventional crops and have a sufficiently synchronised maturity to make mechanical harvesting a viable and economic proposition. Close spacing also hastens the ripening of bulb onions but only when the competition comes from neighbouring onion plants. Weed competition in onions delays maturity and uncontrolled weed growth during the seedling stages can cause complete crop failure since the narrow, erect leaves of the onion plants are unable to shade out and suppress weeds. Broad-leaved crops, beetroot for example, are better able to compete with weeds. Within-row weeds cause less yield reduction than those which develop between the rows since the former have less space and time to establish before they are shaded out by the developing crop plants. The effects of competition between weeds and crop plants will be taken up in more detail in chapter 6. Brussels sprouts grown at close spacings (45 cm × 45 cm) produce evenly developed, small diameter sprouts (19–32 mm) which are ideal for freezing (Thompson and Taylor, 1973). Hearting cabbage and lettuce mature differently from cauliflower and heart up more rapidly at wide spacings. Closely spaced lettuces on the other hand do not heart at all but produce masses of loose leaves.

Maturation of peas and French beans is also influenced by spacing. Plants at close spacings tend to produce their first flush of pods at the same time and inter-plant competition reduces further flowering and pod production. This situation is ideal for producing processing crops which are destructively harvested by machine. Wide spacings encourage sequential flushes of flowers and pods which are suitable for the successive harvests required by fresh markets.

Intercropping

The ground between rows of slow growing, widely spaced crops, such as direct seeded brassicas or bulb onions, can be used to produce rapidly maturing crops such as spinach or radish. Soil surfaces which are not covered by crops are more likely to develop weed canopies, to lose water by evaporation and to suffer erosion damage during heavy rainfall or irrigation.

These can be important problems in the tropics and vegetable growers often overcome them by intercropping (Fordham, 1983). Some of the intensively cropped 'shambas' of Kenya may have three crops growing together e.g. staked tomatoes, cabbage and lettuce.

Maximum utilisation of space is a laudable concept but the main danger of intercropping is that growth of the maincrop will be affected by the short-term crop(s). Sprays which are necessary for one crop may not be suitable or desirable for the others and competition for light, nutrients and water can easily occur.

Bed systems for vegetables

Reference has already been made to the vegetable growing beds of 250 years ago in Britain and to the more recent bed system of carrot growing. This method of production is of course applicable to other vegetables (Ministry of Agriculture, Fisheries and Food, 1971) and is widely used in many parts of the world. Crops are grown in cultivated strips or beds which are straddled by tractors, mounted or trailed implements, and other equipment. Modern tractors will pass over crops up to 60 cm high but even taller crops, such as Brussels sprouts, can be straddled by high clearance tractors. Bed crops are sometimes grown through or under plastic or polythene sheets which promote earliness, conserve moisture and reduce weed competition. Soil compaction is confined to the wheelways which act like a railway system. The railway line effect is so marked that, in the future, bed systems may be used in conjunction with un-manned, remote controlled tractors.

Usually the beds are made during the final cultivations before sowing or planting. It is important that the land is ploughed with a one-way plough which produces a level, even surface. Harrowing and base fertiliser application are completed before the beds are marked out by running the tractor up and down the field. Regularly cropped vegetable soils are often coarse textured and well drained so that clearly defined beds soon develop with the regular passage of machines. A standardised bed width should be used for the whole farm to avoid wheel-changing delays. A 1.80 m wheel centre-to-wheel centre bed is very common and formed the basis of the Fernhurst bed system in England (Lockie, 1959). Narrower beds (1.50 m and 1.40 m) are often used while very wide beds of 2.50 m are occasionally seen. The use of standard width beds of regular length provides a useful method of measuring areas since a particular number of beds constitute a hectare or an acre.

Beds are used in areas of heavy rainfall and irrigation to improve drainage and water removal from the cropped areas. Deep wheelways between raised beds act as channels which carry away excess water. Raised beds may also be made on less well-drained soils where they enable more intensive cropping programmes to be used on sub-optimal land. Special bed-making ploughs and mould boards are used to raise the bed surface at least 15 cm above the wheelways so that the improved drainage encourages earlier warming of the soil, thus permitting earlier sowing or planting.

Bed systems reduce soil compaction and damage in the cropped areas resulting in more even growth and shorter harvesting periods. Organised and mechanically-aided, selective hand harvesting is possible with crops such as lettuce, cabbage or cauliflower which are cut behind trailer-mounted, bed-straddling conveyor collection systems. Alternatively the field-packed cartons of produce may be left in the wheelways to await collection.

Whole beds of carrots or leeks can be machine-lifted in one pass but success of the operation is influenced by bed width, operational depth, crop density, soil type and power of the tractor unit.

Standard rear tyres on commonly used horticultural tractors are about 30 cm wide and low growing, hearting crops of lettuce, cauliflower and cabbage spread laterally into the wheelways where they are soon damaged. At least 45–50 cm should be left between outside rows of adjacent beds and although less crop damage is likely with narrow-wheeled tractors there may be problems of machine stability and additional compaction.

Wide wheelways cause some reductions in the area of cropped land, especially with closely spaced crops such as lettuce, but the plant population can be restored by slightly reducing the within row spacing. Figure 4.4 (parts (a) and (b)) illustrates the situation with lettuce. Figure 4.4(a) shows complete ground coverage with rows and plants 30 cm apart representing a plant population of 110 000 per hectare. Figure 4.4(b) shows five rows of lettuce on a 1.80 m bed which, with plants 30 cm apart in the rows, represents a population of 91 000 per hectare. This represents a 16.6% reduction in population compared with overall coverage but this can be restored by reducing the within-row spacing by a similar percentage i.e. from 30 cm to 25 cm.

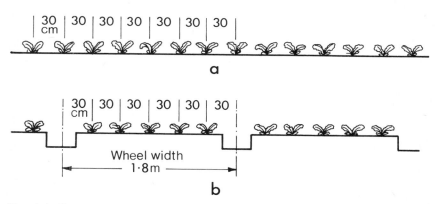

Fig. 4.4. Comparison between (a) complete coverage and (b) a bed system of growing vegetables.

Vegetative propagation

Most vegetable crops are raised from seed but a number are propagated vegetatively. These include Irish and sweet potatoes, rhubarb, Jerusalem and globe artichokes, garlic, shallots, seakale, watercress, mint, thyme, horseradish and other crops.

Vegetative propagation avoids the genetic variation which accompanies propagation from seed. Young vegetatively produced plants are genetically identical with their parent and uniform populations of this type are known as clones. Inspection and selection of healthy material must be done regularly and carefully while trueness-to-type must be continually maintained. A totally uniform population of vegetable plants has many production advantages. They should grow uniformly and mature at the same time. Mechanical harvesting could be used and programmed crop production should be easier. The commercial production of vegetative propagules of a particular crop is unlikely to be undertaken by ordinary growers. Isolation, regular inspection, great attention to detail and perhaps sterile laboratory facilities could be needed by the propagator so that the cost of uniform planting material may be high.

The genetic variation associated with seed raised crops has advantages, however, since individuals have different levels of tolerance to pest and disease attack or to environmental extremes such as cold or heat. Complete crop failure is unlikely.

Degenerative virus diseases are the greatest problem associated with vegetative propagation since material taken from diseased parents will also be infected. Vegetable virus diseases are unlikely to cause plant death but various symptoms, including leaf-rolling, mottling, ring spotting and loss of vigour, will all produce yield reductions. Macro-vegetative propagation is used widely in the commercial production of Irish potatoes with tubers from specially grown mother plants saved as 'seed' for the following season.

Other vegetatively propagated crops are treated similarly with relatively large pieces of propagation material taken from mother plants. Micro-propagation, or tissue culture, also has uses in vegetable production both as a method of rapidly multiplying plants with desirable characteristics (cauliflower, asparagus, Brussels sprouts, etc.) and as a technique for eliminating virus diseases (rhubarb).

Macro-propagation

This term describes the normal types of vegetative propagation for which laboratory facilities are not required.

Irish potatoes and Jerusalem artichokes are propagated from tubers; sweet potatoes, sage, thyme and watercress are raised from stem cuttings; seakale and horseradish from root cuttings; bulbs and cloves are used for shallots and garlic respectively; offsets are taken from globe artichokes while the crowns of rhubarb and the roots of mint are divided and replanted.

Irish potato is probably the most important vegetatively propagated vegetable and commercial growers need a constant supply of virus-free propagation material ('seed') in order to maintain acceptable ware crop yields. Ware producers normally buy certified seed every year or at least every other year. The important virus diseases of potato are aphid transmitted and, in Britain, seed is mainly grown in areas of Scotland, Northern Ireland, Wales and Northern England where climatic conditions limit the aphid populations which are thus more easily controlled. Rigorous inspection, isolation and certification are necesary and an outline of the British system of potato seed production illustrates the requirements.

Production of potato seed begins with a virus-free mother plant which may be a new cultivar from the plant breeder or an existing cultivar which has undergone heat therapy and/or meristem culture.

The cleanest potato tubers are Virus Tested Stem Cutting (VTSC) stocks which are propagated directly from the original mother plant. The cuttings must be free from bacterial and fungal diseases and are rooted under mist in insect-free conditions. After potting up and growing-on, the young plants are transplanted into clean field conditions and sprayed regularly to prevent pest attacks. Tubers from these plants are distributed to specialist growers for multiplication to produce seed which can be certified in the VTSC category.

These tubers are then grown on by high grade propagators to produce Foundation seed. After a number of years of rigorous inspection in the Foundation grade, seed is entered for certification at the Special Stock (SS) levels. Subsequent levels of certification are AA1 (in Scotland only); AA and CC depending on the percentage purity and virus infection of the plants. Seed potatoes may only be grown on land which has not been used for potatoes for four or five years (7 for VTSC) and which has been certified free from potato cyst eelworm (*Heterodera rostochiensis*). Two inspections by Ministry of Agriculture Plant Health officials are required each year for Foundation and Special Stock certification while AA and CC crops are assessed once only. The different tolerance levels for purity and disease are shown in table 4.1

Seed of SS and AA categories is often used by ware growers to produce a market crop from which tubers are saved as 'once-grown' seed, to be planted the following season. Virus disease levels in once-grown seed are usually sufficiently low to allow another good ware crop to be produced.

Bulb onions are usually established from seed but it is also possible to grow them vegetatively from small, immature bulbs called sets. This method is particularly useful for producing onions

Table 4.1 Percentage purity and disease tolerance permitted in different grades of British seed potatoes

Type of seed tolerance	Foundation (%)	Special stock SS (%)	AA (%)	CC (%)
Purity	0.05	0.05	0.10	0.50
Diseases				
Leafroll	0.01 ⎫			
Severe mosaic	nil ⎬	0.02	0.25	2.00
Veinal necrosis	nil ⎭			
Mild Mosaic	0.05	0.25	2.00	10.00
Black leg	0.25	1.00	1.00	4.00
Witches broom	0.02	0.25	0.25	–

in areas with short growing seasons or adverse soil conditions. Sets are produced from seed sown at high densities in a previous season Set size is limited by the competition of close spacing (approximately 1000 per m^2). The sets are field dried, lifted, and then stored at either high (25–30°C) or low (0°C) temperatures to eliminate the risk of flowering when they are replanted.

Macro-propagaton has been used by plant breeders to maintain stocks of parent lines. Isbell (1945) and North (1953) used root cuttings for cabbage and Brussels sprouts respectively while Nieuworf (1969) rooted both Brussels sprout stem cuttings and whole sprouts. Results often varied between cultivars and there were rarely more than 10–20 plants produced from the original parent. Watts and George (1963) grafted portions of autumn cauliflower curds onto potted, glasshouse-raised winter cauliflower rootstocks and obtained shoots within 4–8 weeks.

Micro-propagation

Micro-propagation or tissue culture includes regeneration from single cells or callus and from meristem apices.

Meristem culture has been used to propagate rhubarb (Walkey, 1968), asparagus (Murashige *et al.*, 1972) and cauliflower (Crisp and Walkey, 1974). Apical meristems of heavily virus-infected rhubarb plants are cultured on filter paper bridges in sterile tubes containing a culture solution. Shoots and roots soon develop and the young plants are grown on in sand culture prior to planting outside, (fig. 4.5). The cultured plants are free from turnip mosaic, cherry leafroll, strawberry latent ringspot and cucumber mosaic viruses. Previous methods of apical tip culture had involved the removal of meristematic tissue from plants which had been grown rapidly in high temperatures and light intensities. It was thought that rapid growth produced meristematic tissue which had grown away from the viruses. Recent work suggests that this may not be so and the initial culturing process may either eliminate the diseases or inhibit virus particle multiplication. Virus-free rhubarb has produced 60–90% higher yields of petioles than virus-infected material and root development is so rapid that vegetative propagation by the normal method of division can take place much earlier. The multiplication and distribution of virus-free rhubarb stocks in Britain is controlled by the Nuclear Stock Association and propagation techniques have been devised which allow rapid multiplication from the original virus-free plant. These involve leaf-bud cuttings which, when rooted under mist in a glasshouse, give a 150-fold increase in a year.

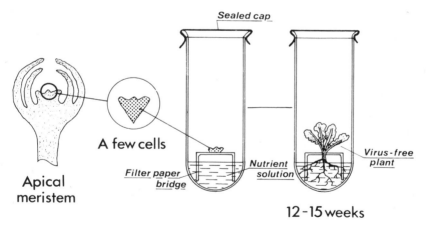

Fig. 4.5. Stages in the meristem culture of rhubarb.

Breeding lines of cauliflower have been maintained and multiplied by micro-propagation methods which utilise the curd. Pow (1969) grew 3–7 mm diameter portions of curd on filter paper bridges in sterile tubes while Crisp and Walkey (1974) devernalised 2 mm diameter portions of curd by shaking them in a culture solution at 20–24°C under supplementary illumination. The high temperatures induce the production of leafy shoots which are removed and rooted in static culture. Division of the leafy shoot tissue and transfer to fresh media can be done several times so that very large numbers (as many as 10 000) of propagules could be produced from a single curd. This type of meristem culture can also be used to produce virus-free clones, and cultured cauliflowers have been freed of turnip mosaic and cauliflower mosaic viruses.

The process of producing genetically identical clones of vegetable plants by micro-propagation is a valuable research tool currently used by plant breeders, virologists and others. Micro-propagation of the large quantities of uniform planting material necessary for commercial vegetable growing is expensive but the advantages of clonal material may eventually make this a viable proposition. Progress in this direction has been recently achieved by the *in vitro* production of minute potato tubers which could lead to direct 'seeding' of this crop (Wang and Hu, 1982).

Propagation from seed

Most vegetable crops are established from seed although the seed is often produced in different parts of the world from where the vegetables are to be grown. Seed production and the development of new cultivars is covered in more detail in chapter 12. Seed quality and performance are affected by a wide range of genetic and environmental factors.

Effect of mother plant

Well grown, pest- and disease-free mother plants produce the best seed. Parent plant nutrition can affect seed performance but major effects only result from severe nutrient deficiencies. Seeds with low phosphorus contents are likely to cause the greatest reductions to subsequent crop growth and yield. Environmental effects on seed formation and subsequent performance have been reviewed by Austin (1972). Genetic variation between seeds can affect germination, emergence performance and vigour, all of which will have important effects on final crop development. There are great potential benefits to be achieved from selecting for uniformity of emergence and high seed vigour. Seed performance is also influenced by its original position on the parent plant although there are variations between species. Seeds of carrot and celery produced on the primary umbels have larger embryos compared with those from secondary and higher order umbels, and usually produce the largest seedlings, although the relationship may be more complex with the time of seed formation being as important as final seed size in some instances. Uniformity of seedling emergence and size is often more important than absolute size and there is evidence that selecting and controlling the growth of seed plants could lead to the production of seed with less variable seedling characteristics.

Seed dormancy

A viable seed which does not germinate when given the necessary favourable conditions is said to exhibit dormancy, a state which may either be innate or induced. The seeds of many vegetable crops have innate dormancy when removed from the parent plant but this is quickly overcome by a period of drying and after-ripening. In tropical countries this may take place rapidly and seeds released into the soil when one vegetable (e.g. marrows) is ploughed in can emerge as weeds in the next crop. Hard seed coats may prevent water inbibition and delay germination. This phenomenon is unusual in vegetables but can occur in some of the hard seeded tropical leguminous crops. The seed coat can usually be softened by soaking in water or mechanically weakened by scarification but difficult subjects may require treatments which involve soaking the hard seeds in concentrated sulphuric acid.

Natural dormancy creates a break between plant life cycles and ensures that seed germination and seedling emergency only occur when environmental conditions are suitable. Hard seed coats are softened naturally by off-season soil conditions while other kinds of dormancy are controlled by chemical inhibitors which are either on or in the seed and whose action disappears as dormancy progresses. Artificial removal or reversal of inhibitory processes may be used to improve germination and emergence and the techniques are discussed later in the chapter.

Germination

Germination is difficult to define since it can mean different things to different groups of people. Research workers may consider it to have occurred when the radicle has emerged from the seed coat while vegetable growers are more likely to regard seedling emergence through the soil surface as evidence of germination. A grower's livelihood depends on the availability of seed of high quality and germination percentage. Legislation exists to ensure that marketed vegetable seed reaches the necessary standards and testing procedures are available by which the potential field performance of seed can be predicted with some confidence. These aspects are dealt with more fully in chapter 12. The remainder of the present chapter deals with physiological factors influencing germination and reviews available methods for improving seed performance in the field.

The germination process requires moisture, oxygen and temperature ranges which are specific to particular crops. Water is imbibed and activates growth processes, the rate of which are very temperature-dependent. Germination rate usually increases until the temperature reaches 30–35°C but imbibing seeds of crops such as lettuce exhibit thermodormancy at the higher range. Lettuce types vary in response to high temperature with cos and typical British butterhead (smooth leaved) types failing to germinate above 25°C while crisphead types still germinate well at 30°C. Freshly harvested lettuce seed shows thermodormancy at even lower temperatures (20°C). The temperature-sensitive stages of lettuce germination last only 8–16 hours and subsequent plant growth can occur at much higher temperatures (35–40°C). Thermodormancy can be minimised by choice of the appropriate variety, reducing the soil temperature (usually by irrigation) at the appropriate time, sowing late in the day when temperatures are falling, imbibing seeds at low temperatures (2°C) and redrying before sowing or soaking seeds with a mixture of 5 ppm gibberellic acid plus kinetin before sowing (Gray and Steckel, 1975).

The effects of soil temperature on germination of other vegetables is shown in fig. 4.6. Celery, onions and leeks will germinate very well over a very narrow range while brassicas, peas and broad beans are very adaptable. Cucumbers, marrows, peppers, French and runner beans, sweet corn and tomatoes do not like low temperatures and crop failures often result from sowings made in cold soils, especially if the conditions are also wet.

Light is required for the germination of some vegetable seeds but there are considerable variations even between cultivars of a particular crop. Germination of some cultivars of celery (particularly at temperatures above 15°C), tomato and lettuce (particularly when freshly harvested) is reduced in the dark. Light is unable to penetrate more than about 5 mm into the soil and the performance of light-sensitive cultivars of celery is markedly reduced when they are direct seeded. This is one of the major drawbacks with direct seeding celery but the light requirement can be overcome by

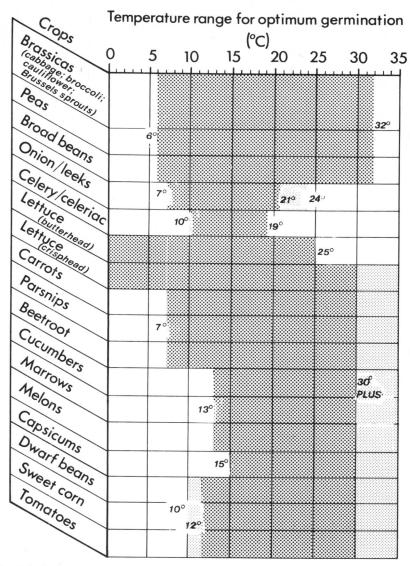

Fig. 4.6. Influence of soil temperature on vegetable seed germination. Darker shading indicates optimum range but germination also takes place at values indicated by lighter shading.

soaking seeds in a mixture of gibberellins ($GA_{4/7}$) before sowing (Thomas *et al.*, 1972). The thermodormancy factor may be further reduced when the following growth regulators are included in the gibberellin solution in which seeds are presoaked.

ethephon   – 2-chloroethylphosphonic acid (Ethrel)
daminozide   – N-dimethylaminosuccinamic acid (B-Nine)
BAP   – 6-benzylamino purine

Germination alone, however, is insufficient to guarantee good establishment in the field as this is also dependent on seed vigour. The International Seed Testing Association defines seed vigour as 'the sum total of those properties of the seed which determine the potential level of activity and performance of the seed or seed lot during germination and seedling emergence'. The effects of low seed vigour are most likely to be apparent when seeds are sown under adverse conditions. A number of factors can contribute to seed vigour and the contribution of the mother plant, including location of the original inflorescence, have already been referred to.

Seed size

Seed size and weight are usually positively correlated and the largest and heaviest are likely to have the highest laboratory germination. It does not follow that they will also give the best field emergence. Hewston (1964) illustrated this fact with summer cauliflower. Similar work with radish showed that large seeds produce earlier maturing crops than small seeds. This may be because radish grows and matures very quickly and any advantages conferred by large seeds are easily carried through to harvest. It is, therefore, worth grading radish seed into three size groups – large, medium and small – and sowing the samples separately.

Mixed size seed (ungraded) is likely to emerge irregularly with the earliest seedlings growing away quickly and hindering the development of those which emerge later. The use of size-graded seed can overcome this problem.

Seed storage

Seed deterioration begins on the parent plant and is accelerated by pest or disease attack, mechanical damage and high temperatures but seed moisture content and temperature are the most important factors which influence longevity. These aspects are referred to later in the chapter on vegetable seed production (chapter 12).

Seed treatments which improve emergence

Sowing untreated, dry seed often leads to variable emergence of seedlings particularly when soil and seed factors are suboptimal. Satisfactory crop growth only occurs during periods of suitable growing conditions and short growing seasons may make it impossible to grow some vegetables in particular locations. Quicker seedling emergence may give sufficient time for otherwise impossible crops to be grown while earlier, synchronised crop emergence enables leaf canopies to develop more rapidly so that plants are better able to convert radiant energy into harvestable products.

Certain types of vegetable production need precise control over plant populations in order to govern crop size and development while synchronised crop maturity is needed for 'once-over' mechanical harvesting. This is particularly true for processing crops (vining peas, dwarf beans, sweet corn, etc.) and fresh market root and bulb crops (carrots, beetroot, bulb onions, etc.) but more precise, programmed production is now being demanded for crops such as cabbage, cauliflower, lettuce and celery which are traditionally selectively hand harvested.

Variations in crop development and maturity are influenced by variable growing conditions but uniform development is more likely if plant establishment variability is eliminated. Uniform-sized plants can be transplanted but this is expensive and labour intensive so efforts have been made to improve and synchronise seedling emergence.

Soaking in water
Beetroot 'seeds' are really fruits which contain two or three seeds within a corky pericarp. The fruits are irregularly shaped and are often mechanically rubbed by seedsmen to produce a more spherical unit which can be size graded and space sown. The pericarp contains water-soluble germination inhibitors which can be washed out by soaking the 'seeds' in running water at 21°C for an hour before sowing.

Treatment with nutrient solutions
Ells (1963) hastened the emergence of tomato seedlings at low temperatures (10°C) by wetting the seed with hypertonic nutrient solutions of 1–2% tripotassium orthophosphate ($K_3PO_4H_2O$) and 0.5–2% potassium nitrate (KNO_3) and then redrying before sowing. Emergence rate was up to 5 days quicker but the number of

emerged seedlings was reduced by up to 30% after 19 days. Water is imbibed and enzymes activated during the pre-sowing wetting but the nutrients maintain a high osmotic pressure around the seed and prevent the entry of sufficient water to permit germination at that stage.

Wetting with water and redrying
Alternate wetting and drying of seeds before sowing was claimed by Russian workers (Genkel *et al.*, 1964) to confer drought hardiness on the ensuing crop. Three cycles of this technique, which is often referred to as either 'hardening' or 'advancing', improved the rate of emergence in carrots and gave a 10% increase in yield. Hardening increases embryo size which in turn gives rise to quicker germination and seedling emergence.

Priming with polyethylene glycol
Heydecker *et al.* (1973) devised the technique of placing seeds in contact with solutions of a high molecular weight fraction of polyethylene glycol (PEG, marketed as 'Carbowax 6000'). Very rapid germination follows treatment in solutions with osmotic potentials of −10 to −15 bars for between seven and twenty-one days (fourteen on average), depending on the vegetable species.

The principle is similar to that of Ells with the PEG solution acting as a germination barrier. Seeds take up sufficient water to reach the 'brink of germination' but are prevented from taking up any more until the PEG solution is removed. Rapid and synchronous germination then follows and 50% of viable celery seed will germinate in forty-eight hours after treatment. The best results are obtained when the seeds are surface dried before sowing rather than being completely redried and stored.

Germination improvements have been recorded with many vegetables including beetroot, carrot, onion, and celery. Priming could be used to stimulate rapid and synchronous germination of seeds prior to fluid drilling, a method to be discussed later.

Treatment with growth regulators
The use of mixtures of gibberellins and other growth regulators to break thermodormancy and allow natural celery seed to germinate in the dark has already been mentioned. The treatment can also be used with pelleted celery seeds, when germination improvements of more than 40% are found over untreated pelleted seed. Natural celery seed is small and irregularly shaped so there are difficulties

with precision, space sowing and celery crops are usually trans-planted. Pelleting standardises the shape but often reduces germination and emergence and a pre-pelleting seed treatment with growth regulators is very useful. It is now possible for celery to be accurately direct seeded while plant raising is easier when pelleted seed with a high germination capacity is sown directly into peat or soil blocks.

Plug-mix planting
Direct seeding of tomatoes often results in problems of poor emergence, lack of uniformity and difficulties in achieving target populations. Plug-mix planting involves mixing seed with a moistened artificial carrier compost containing peat, vermiculite, perlite, lime, fertiliser and fungicide. The seed is uniformly mixed in the compost from which 25–50 ml volume plugs are made and precision planted. There are several seeds in each plug and clumps of seedlings emerge at each station. Acceptable populations of tomatoes are achieved in this way but the use of untreated natural seed still creates problems of irregular emergence.

Pre-germination of the tomato seed before it is added to the compost mix produces more rapid (five days in ideal conditions) and synchronous emergence. Tomato plants will grow at temperatures below those necessary for satisfactory germination and pre-germination before plug-mix planting overcomes the problems of early-season cold soils.

Pre-germination and fluid drilling
The pre-sowing treatments described above can improve the rate and uniformity of seedling emergence but will not overcome the problem of non-viable seeds, whose presence can cause the production of a gappy stand of plants. Pre-germination of the seed has the potential to overcome this problem and is also used to counter the difficulties of thermodormancy in lettuce, light and high temperature requirements of celery and temperature sensitivity of tomatoes.

The technique and drilling equipment were originally devised by Elliott (1966) for sowing seed in an aqueous solution into killed grass swards. Currah *et al.* (1974) modified the equipment and demonstrated the value of fluid drilling germinating seeds of vegetables. Further research at the National Vegetable Research Station in England has developed fluid drilling into a commercially viable technique (Gray, 1981).

Seeds are germinated in controlled environments where optimum conditions of light, temperature and aeration can be provided. Germinating seeds are then separated from the remainder by their differential resistance to water. The emerged radicles of germinating seeds provide extra resistance to a stream of water flowing through sloping tubes and are carried along while the ungerminated seeds remain behind.

Germinated seeds of most vegetables can be stored at low temperatures (1°C) in water or high humidity conditions if conditions for drilling are unfavourable. Tomato, sweet corn and bean seeds are cold sensitive and should not be stored below 6°C. Seeds of several species have been stored for seven to ten days without damage or loss of vigour.

The germinated seeds are mixed into a protective gel immediately prior to drilling. Alginate gels were used initially but many other materials have now been tested with mineral colloid and poly-acrylate gels giving consistently better seedling emergence than alginates. Thorough mixing and correct gel consistency ensures that seeds remain evenly suspended during drilling.

The early types of fluid drill extruded gel with a random distribution of seeds. Non-precision drilling is suitable for crops such as radish and salad onions but space sowing is required for the majority of vegetable crops in Britain. Equipment is under development which is able to handle single germinated seeds thus making precision fluid drilling a possibility.

Fluid drilling germinating seeds produces earlier emergence in widely varying soil conditions. More uniform emergence can also occur and produce uniform growth of some crops right through until harvesting. Continuity of production and the prospects for mechanical harvesting of lettuce are improved and the effective length of the temperate growing season is increased for tomatoes and other crops which only germinate at high soil temperatures.

Research in the United Kingdom has demonstrated five to twelve day earlier emergence and up to 20% increase in total emergence of carrots while celery has emerged up to twenty-one days earlier with an increase of up to 58% in the total number of seedlings emerging. Onions and parsnips emerge fifteen to eighteen days earlier especially from early sowings made at the start of the growing season. Lettuce emerge more synchronously and mature more uniformly and up to eight days earlier than traditional dry-seeded crops. Pre-germinated tomato seed emerges rapidly in Britain and outdoor production of this crop from direct seeding is now a viable proposition for either the fresh or processing markets.

Direct seeding pre-germinated seeds has important implications for extending growing seasons and allowing the grower more accurate control over crop production but there are other prospects. Materials such as fertilisers for seedling growth, fungicides, insecticides or growth regulating compounds could be incorporated with the seed–gel mix and provide a completely artificial environment around the seed. Inoculation of French bean seed with *Rhizobium* bacteria before fluid drilling has been mentioned in a previous chapter.

Care of pre-germinated seed following drilling is particularly important since dry soil conditions cause severe losses. Irrigation is an almost essential management tool for fluid drilled vegetables and the more precise and controlled production potential is only realised with accurate and attentive management inputs.

Seed treatments which improve accuracy of spacing

Treatments which improve seed performance are important but accurate plant spacing is equally vital to ensure the most efficient use of resources and to produce specific types of vegetables to pre-determined programmes. Techniques are therefore needed which enable seeds to be placed into the soil in pre-determined patterns and spacings.

Taped seed
Water-soluble tapes and glues are used with the seeds attached to the tape at the required intervals. American-devised plastic tapes are available on reels which hold 1500–6000 m and drilling involves unreeling the tape into furrows formed by specially designed drills. In Britain the results with beetroot, lettuce and cabbage have been worse than those from normal drilling methods. There have been problems of erratic performance caused by variable depths of 'drilling', uneven supplies of soil moisture causing variations in seed release and poor shelf life of the tape. The use of pre-sown paper or plastic sheets for sowing boxes of vegetables or bedding plants is an adaptation of the taped seed principle.

Size-graded natural seed
Machinery for seed drilling is discussed in chapter 11 but some of

the currently available precision drilling equipment requires seed to be more or less spherical and of uniform size. Brassica crops are amongst the few vegetables which have naturally spherical seeds. Others such as leek, onion, radish and pea are almost spherical while those of sweet corn and other legumes are sufficiently large to prevent more than one going into each hole in the cell wheel or belt. Seed size varies considerably between different cultivars of the same vegetable species and even between different seed lots of the same cultivar. Garthwaite (1967) showed that brassicas can have some seeds which are twice as big as others in the same sample. The variable seed numbers per unit weight in different cultivars of Brussels sprouts, cabbage and leeks are shown in table 4.2.

Table 4.2   Seed size variations with vegetable crops

Vegetables	Cultivar	Seed number per kg in '000's
Brussels sprouts	Darkmar 21	312.4
	Irish Elegance	217.8
Cabbage	Durham Early	250.0
	Golden Acre	198.2
Leek	Wintercrop	429.0
	Empire	374.0

These seed size and count variations are not acceptable for use with belt or cell wheel spacing drills and the seed must be size graded. Mixed size seed samples produce variable seedling emergence and size grading will produce more uniform performance of any natural seed.

Pelleted seed
Irregularly-shaped seed can either be drilled in the natural state, which makes precision sowing very difficult with belt or cell wheel drills, or the shape can be altered so that it is acceptable for the drill. The most usual method of changing the shape involves encasing the seed with an inert clay-like material to form a pellet which must break down rapidly in the soil but retain stability and shape during handling and drilling. Seed of lettuce and Umbelliferous crops, such

as carrot, celery and parsnip, is generally available in pelleted forms but seed houses may also supply onions, leeks and other species as pellets.

Three types of pelleted seed are generally available. The large, full coat pellets have seeds covered with a large volume of material. They are very spherical in shape and are usually in the 3.75 mm to 4.75 mm size range. There are 13 000–17 000 large lettuce pellets per kg which means that individual pellets are 40–50 times heavier than natural seeds. Less pelleting material is used in mini-pellets which are roughly oval and follow the general shape of the raw seed. Mini-pellets of lettuce are 10–15 times heavier than natural lettuce seed so that there are 40 000–65 000 mini-pellets per kg. They cannot be precision drilled as accurately as the larger spherical pellets but the manufacturers claim a 70% single spacing. Split pellets are round to oval and split open and release the seeds very rapidly in reasonably moist conditions. They are size graded (2.75–3.50 mm) for lettuce with 20 000–30 000 pellets per kg.

Pelleting often causes poor, erratic germination and emergence in dry soil conditions, since quite large quantities of water are required before the pellets break down fully to release the seeds. Intermittent supplies of water are not satisfactory since the pellets are likely to become leathery and never break down. It is safer to use natural seed during dry conditions if regular irrigation is not available.

Some of the germination and emergence problems may be overcome by treating the seeds with growth regulating compounds before pelleting.

Rubbed and graded 'seed'

Beetroot fruits are irregularly shaped and multi-germ types contain two or three 'seeds' within the corky pericarp. The fruits are sown as 'seeds' and two or three seedlings often emerge at each station. Such clumping could be avoided by using mono-germ types (one seed per fruit) but few mono-germ beetroot cultivars are available at present.

Natural beetroot 'seeds' range in diameter from 2.25–6.50 mm and cannot be accurately space sown. Seedsmen will remove the corners of the corky material and the rubbed 'seeds' can then be size graded prior to space sowing. Rubbed and graded beetroot is usually in the 2.75–3.50 mm or 3.50–4.25 mm size range with 100 000–150 000 or 50 000–100 000 'seeds' per kg respectively. There are usually between 40 000 and 150 000 natural 'seeds' per kg.

Seed treatments for pest and disease control

Soil or seed borne pests and diseases can cause considerable damage during the development of a crop. Many of these problems can be avoided, or at least reduced, using relatively inexpensive seed treatments prior to sowing. Examples of such treatments are included under the topic of pest and disease control in chapter 6.

References and further reading

Austin, R.B. (1972) 'Effects of environment before harvesting on viability'. In *Viability of Seeds*, ed. E. H. Roberts. London: Chapman and Hall, 114–149.

Bleasdale, J.K.A. (1965) 'Relationships between set characteristics and yield in maincrop potatoes'. *Journal of Agricultural Science*, **64**, 361–366.

Bleasdale, J.K.A. (1966) 'The effects of plant spacing on the yield of bulb onions (*Allium cepa* L.) grown from seed'. *Journal of Horticultural Science*, **41**, 145–153.

Bleasdale, J.K.A. (1967) 'Systematic designs for spacing experiments'. *Experimental Agriculture*, **3**, 73–86.

Bleasdale, J.K.A. (1968) 'Effect of plant spacing on the yield and profitability of the scarlet runner bean (*Phaseolus multiflorus*)'. *Horticultural Research*, **8**, 155–169.

Bleasdale, J.K.A. (1970) 'Importance of plant population for improved vegetable production'. *Journal of National Institute of Agricultural Botany*, **12**, Supplement, 35–39.

Bleasdale, J.K.A. (1973a) 'Some problems and prospects in plant spacing'. *Journal of the Royal Agricultural Society*, **134**, 89–100.

Bleasdale, J.K.A. (1973b) *Plant Physiology in Relation to Horticulture*. London: Macmillan.

Bleasdale, J.K.A. and Thompson, R. (1966) 'The effects of plant density and the pattern of plant arrangement on the yield of parsnips'. *Journal of Agricultural Science*, **41**, 371–378.

Crisp, P. and Walkey, D.G.A. (1974) 'The use of aseptic meristem culture in cauliflower breeding'. *Euphytica*, **23**, 305–313.

Currah, I.E. (1975) *Some factors affecting the size of plants in the carrot crop*. Ph.D. thesis, University of London.

Currah, I.E., Gray, D. and Thomas, T.H. (1974) 'The sowing of germinating vegetable seeds using a fluid drill'. *Annals of Applied Biology*, **76**, 311–318.

Elliott, J.G. (1966) 'The sowing of seeds in aqueous fluid'. *Report of Weed Research Organisation*, Oxford 1965/66, 31–32.

Ells, J.E. (1963) 'The influence of treating tomato seed with nutrient solution on emergence rate and seedling growth'. *Proceedings of American Society of Horticultural Science*, **83**, 684–687.

Fordham, R. (1983) 'Intercropping – what are the advantages?' *Outlook on Agriculture*, **12**, 142–146.

Frappell, B.D. (1968) *Plant density studies with red beet*. M.Sc. thesis. University of Birmingham.

Garthwaite, J.M. (April 1967) 'It's for every grower to weigh the pros and cons'. *Commercial Grower*, 882–885.

Genkel, P.A., Martyanova, K.L. and Zubova, L.A. (1964) 'Production experiments on pre-sowing drought hardening of plants'. *Fiz. Rast.*, **11**, 538.

Gray, D. (1976) 'The effect of time to emergence on head weight at maturity in lettuce (*Lactuca sativa*)'. *Annals of Applied Biology*, **82**, 569–575.

Gray, D. (1981) 'Fluid drilling of vegetable seeds'. *Horticultural Reviews*, **3**, 1–27.

Gray, D. and Steckel, J.R.A. (1975) 'High temperature-induced dormancy in lettuce'. *Report of National Vegetable Research Station*, Wellesbourne, Warwick, for 1974, 78–79.

Hewston, L.J. (1964) *Effects of seed size on germination, emergence and yield of some vegetable crops*. M.Sc. thesis, University of Birmingham.

Heydecker, W., Higgins, J. and Gulliver, R.L. (1973) 'Accelerated germination by osmotic seed treatment'. *Nature (London)*, **246**, 42–44.

Isbell, G.L. (1945) 'Propagating cabbage by root cuttings'. *Proceedings of American Society of Horticultural Science*, **46**, 341–344.

Lockie, G.D. (1959) 'The Fernhurst bed system of market gardening'. *Journal of Royal Horticultural Society*, **84**, 231–234.

Ministry of Agriculture, Fisheries and Food (1969) *The Bed System of Carrot Growing*. S.T. Leaflet 27, Pinner, Middlesex.

Ministry of Agriculture, Fisheries and Food (1971) *Vegetable Growing on the Bed System*. S.T. Leaflet 137, Pinner, Middlesex.

Murashige, T., Shabde, M.N., Hasegawa, P.M., Takatori, F.H. and Jones, J.B. (1972) 'Propagation of asparagus through shoot apex culture'. *Journal of American Society of Horticultural Science*, **97**, 158–161.

Nelder, J.A. (1962) 'New kinds of systematic designs for spacing experiments'. *Biometrics*, **18**, 283–307.

Nieuworf, M. (1969) '*Cole Crops*', World Crops series, London: Leonard Hill, pp. 223–238.

North, C. (1953) 'Experiments with root cuttings of Brussels sprouts'. *Annals of Applied Biology*, **40**, 250–261.

Pow, J.J. (1969) 'Clonal propagation *in vitro* from cauliflower curd'. *Horticultural Research*, **9**, 151–152.

Salter, P.J. (1971) 'Minicauliflowers'. *Agriculture (London)*, **78**, 231–235.

Thomas, T.H., Palevitch, D. and Austin, R.B. (1972) 'Stimulation of celery seed germination with plant growth regulators'. *Proceedings 11th British Weed Control Conference*, British Crop Protection Council, 760–765.

Thompson, R. and Taylor, H. (1973) 'The effects of population and harvest date on the yields and size grading of an F_1 hybrid and an open-pollinated Brussels sprout cultivar'. *Journal of Horticultural Science*, **48**, 235–246.

Walkey, D.G.A. (1968) 'The production of virus-free rhubarb by apical tip culture'. *Journal of Horticultural Science*, **43**, 283–287.

Wang, P.J. and Hu, C.Y. (1982) '*In vitro* mass tuberization and virus seed potato production in Taiwan'. *American Potato Journal*, **59**, 33–39.

Watts, L.E. and George, R.A.T. (1963) 'Vegetative propagation of autumn cauliflower'. *Euphytica*, **12**, 341–345.

Warne, L.G.C. (1951) 'Spacing experiments on vegetables. III. The growth and yield of shallots in relation to spacing, manuring and size of planting material'. *Journal of Horticultural Science*, **26**, 285–295.

5   Plant establishment

Introduction

Vegetable plants may be raised on the farm or bought in as young plants for transplanting but, more frequently, establishment is from seed sown directly into the final growing positions. The seeding technique is commonly called 'direct drilling' but this term can be confusing since in some parts of the world it is also applied to the system of sowing crops directly into soil which has received very little or even no cultivation. This latter type of direct drilling is mainly used for large-scale field production of arable crops like cereals but, as vegetables are increasingly being grown on arable farming enterprises it could be a misleading term. Confusion can be avoided by referring to vegetable establishment from seed as 'direct seeding'.

Although systems of direct drilling or minimum cultivation are particularly important for extensive arable crop production there may also be possible uses in the area of field vegetable growing. Tractors and other power units used in arable cropping become larger and heavier every year. Primary cultivation of the soil is the aspect of crop production which usually requires the most mechanical power and farmers or growers tend to choose large tractors and cultivating equipment so that operations can be completed as quickly and efficiently as possible. Subsequent crop production operations, such as spraying, fertiliser top dressing or mechanical weed control, do not require very large power units. Heavy equipment which compacts and smears the land during wet soil conditions, which is when primary cultivations are often done, can cause considerable damage to soil structure and drainage. This is particularly so on intensively cultivated vegetable farms where it is increasingly difficult to maintain structure by incorporating heavy applications of organic matter or by making regular use of grass ley. Using lighter tractors and cultivating equipment would reduce the problems but would necessitate the use of different or slower systems of primary soil cultivation. Direct drilling of vegetable crops would seem to be most appropriate in locations where wet conditions consistently delay cultivations or where there are severe problems with soil structure. Results with green peas and Brussels sprouts have been promising.

The choice between direct seeding and transplanting

Large-scale arable farmers are more familir with direct seeding than transplanting as a means of crop establishment. Production methods of cereals, root crops, grass, etc., are based on sequences of direct seeding, spraying for pest, disease and weed control, and combine harvesting. Similar sequences are likely to be demanded for vegetable crops which farmers intend to include in extensive arable cropping rotations. If additional, labour-intensive cultural operations are necessary then vegetables are likely to be a less attractive farming proposition. This generalisation may be conditioned by other factors such as land or labour availability and potential crop returns. Vegetables are usually transplanted in Japan but traditional arable crops, such as sugar beet, are also planted so that crop throughput and land use are maximised.

Increasing attention to detail is being shown with traditionally direct seeded cereal crops which can now be space sown to establish a pre-determined population of plants, shoots and ears per unit area. Widespread introductions of transplanting into large-scale arable farming are unlikely but recent developments in fluid-drilling, raising plants in blocks, and automatic transplanting may be applicable to certain types of extensive crop production.

Transplanting requires more labour than direct seeding but plants occupy their final positions for shorter periods and may allow other crops to be grown beforehand. In tropical or subtropical areas where irrigation is available it may be possible to direct seed most vegetables since the temperatures are usually suitable for good germination, emergence and subsequent growth. Direct seeded crops avoid the problems of transplanting checks which, although cultural and chemical treatments can help, are particularly severe in hot, dry conditions. Direct seeding necessitates earlier and larger scale preparation of seedbeds and this can be difficult on some soils in climates where the length of the growing season is limited. Transplanting can be very important in such locations or where the area available for producing vegetables is restricted.

Plant growth rate is related to the efficiency with which increasing radiation is intercepted and converted into useful plant products. Direct seeded crops often grow slowly through the seedling stages and show poor light interception with much of the radiation falling on bare soil and being wasted. Light interception improves directly with leaf canopy cover until a point is reached where mutual shading reduces the functioning efficiency of lower leaves. The ratio of leaf area to the area of ground covered is known as the Leaf Area Index (LAI) and maximum assimilation will usually occur on LAI of about 5, although species will differ a little. This is particularly relevant for crops, such as Brussels sprouts, cabbage, cauliflower, etc., which form a dense, spreading canopy and it is desirable that the optimum LAI is achieved as quickly as possible. Transplanted vegetables produce the necessary leaf canopy much faster than seeded crops and retain this advantage provided there are no post-planting checks, crop growth restriction or unacceptable maturity characteristics. The interaction between optimum LAI, the need for rapid growth and length of growing season is also seen with upright-growing crops such as bulb onions. The necessary ware bulb size from early maturing crops grown in Britain is likely to be achieved with more certainty from planted rather than direct seeded plants. Transplants which are produced under protection, either in a seedbed or in containers, can be planted as soon as outside conditions are suitable. Programmed production of transplants is easier under protection and specialist plant raisers often supply farmers in important vegetable growing districts. It may be necessary to slow down the growth of transplants if field conditions are not suitable for planting. The amount of time taken to produce vegetable transplants, and therefore, the time for which the eventual planting site is available for other crops, varies with location, season and the vegetable species. In locations where temperatures average 10–15°C, brassica plants can be produced in between six and eight weeks from outdoor seedbeds, whereas leek plants will require a month longer in similar conditions. Production of lettuce plants in peat blocks under protection can take between three and six weeks depending on season and the protection facilities available.

Growers of rapidly-maturing intensive vegetables on early soils are likely to prefer transplanting since it allows more crops to be grown on a particular piece of land in a given time. Increased crop throughput may provide sufficient incentive to encourage large-scale growers to change from direct seeding to transplanting, particularly if there are prospects of reducing the transplanting

labour requirements. The increased use of peat-block-raised vegetable transplants in Britain during the late 1970s illustrates the
attraction and potential value of rapid throughput. The precise
target plant populations required for controlled production programmes are usually easier to achieve by transplanting. This is
particularly true with difficult-to-germinate crops such as celery,
which are rarely direct seeded. Nevertheless pre-sowing seed
treatments are improving the certainty of germination and emergence.

Seed costs may influence the choice between direct seeding and
transplanting. In spite of modern developments it is still impossible
to sow one seed where each plant is finally needed and direct
seeding uses more seed than transplanting even when crops are
space sown. Drilling patterns are frequently devised to allow at least
three seeds to produce one final plant. The extra seed may not
represent a great increase in total production costs but the figure can
be quite significant when expensive, F_1 hybrid seed is used. When
seedbed and planting losses are also considered it is likely that direct
seeding will use up to five times as much seed as transplant raising to
establish a crop. Seed germination, seedling vigour and the
efficiency of seedbed and post-planting care all influence the amount
of extra seed required but when it is expensive there are advantages
and benefits from sowing it into carefully managed and maintained
seedbeds. Even more attention to detail is possible by raising plants
in containers, blocks or in the border soil within heated or unheated
structures.

The area of seedbed required will be small compared with the
final cropped area. A hectare of outdoor brassica seedbed with rows
30 cm apart should produce sufficient transplants for 25–70 hectares
assuming final populations of 17 000–47 000 per hectare. It is
relatively easy to pay great attention to detail with such small
seedbed areas. Plant root development is encouraged by adding
peat, sand, grit, etc., to the top 10 cm of the soil and irrigation
should be available to help rapid germination, uniform emergence
and uninterrrupted seedling growth. Competition between crop
plant seedlings in seedbeds is more likely when they are sown close
together. Space sowing reduces the danger but plants must be
transplanted at a sufficiently early stage to avoid overcrowding
which causes weak, spindly growth and encourages pest and disease
build-up. Crop seedling competition is unlikely with direct seeded
vegetables which are space sown but there are risks when very dense
lines of plants are produced for subsequent thinning.

Pest, disease and weed control are important factors during plant establishment. Direct seeded crops occupy larger areas for longer periods and very rigorous crop protection measures are essential particularly in space sown crops where fewer losses can be tolerated. Effective weed control is necessary from the earliest stages with direct seeded vegetables since subsequent or remedial programmes are often difficult, expensive or impossible. Crop protection and weed control are easier on compact seedbed areas while any intensive remedial measures are more justified and easier to effect. Strict control of seedbed pathogens is necessary otherwise the problems will be transferred to the final growing quarters. A small area of infected seedbed will produce enough diseased transplants to cause problems in large areas of the final cropping site. The difficulties are compounded when the seedbed pathogens are soil borne and difficult to eradicate, e.g. club root of brassicas (*Plasmodiophora brassicae*) and white rot of onions (*Sclerotium cepivorum*).

Plant establishment methods influence the type of root system produced. Direct seeded plants usually have large tap roots while transplanted crops have shallower and more fibrous systems, (Rickard, 1972). Maintenance of moisture near to the soil surface is important for fibrous-rooted plants which are also more easily damaged by surface cultivations. There are indications that the larger, deeper and undisturbed root systems of direct seeded brassicas are better able to withstand attacks by the larvae of cabbage root fly (*Delia radicum*).

Plant establishment and crop maturation

Direct seeding often produces earlier and more uniform crop maturation than transplanting. This has been demonstrated for a number of autumn cauliflower varieties by Salter and Fradgley (1969) who also showed that increasing plant competition in the seedbed and increasing the age of transplants also contributed to delays in maturity. Direct seeded cauliflowers frequently have shorter maturity periods than transplanted crops and the use of size-graded seed produces even more uniformity. Direct seeding has produced cauliflower crops with up to 80% of the curds ready for cutting at one time (Salter and Ward, 1972). This high percentage makes once-over mechanical harvesting a technically and economically viable proposition and also allows accurate planning of production programmes. Unfortunately curd development and maturation are usually more variable than this and continuous and regular production of scheduled supplies of cauliflower remains a problem. Curd initiation in cauliflowers is affected by many factors including temperature, variety and stage of plant development. Physiological state of the plants is more important than morphological size or chronological age and uniform maturation only occurs if all the plants initiate curds at the same time. Possible methods of achieving this are discussed later.

Gray (1978) has also stressed the importance of uniform germination and synchronous emergence in producing evenly maturing crops of direct seeded lettuce. Size and uniformity of transplants is particularly important with vegetables which are grown for vegetative characteristics, e.g. lettuce, cabbage or leeks. Seedling selection and grading prior to transplanting vegetative vegetables reduces maturation irregularities. Successful programming and continuity of production with planted rather than direct seeded lettuce is shown by Heath (1978). Traditional systems of transplanting are expensive, however, and may only be justified when guaranteed markets are assured (Eastwood and Gray, 1976).

Leeks have long growing periods and can be harvested at various stages of development. Direct seeded crops avoid transplanting checks and produce good early yields but planted crops catch up later in the season.

Celery has small seeds which usually germinate slowly and emerge irregularly after direct seeding. Consequently crops are usually transplanted but uniformly maturing celery crops can be produced from direct seeding if seedling emergence is synchronised (Rickard, 1972).

Sowing and planting schedules

Vegetable market outlets increasingly demand programmed crop production to meet specific demands. This is obviously very important for processing crops but supermarket chains and other fresh market outlets are also requiring vegetables to be grown to schedules.

Attempts to maintain continuity of supply are frequently based on sowings or plantings made at regular intervals with a range of cultivars. The quantities produced are usually controlled by adjusting the areas of different cultivars while short- and medium-term storage are sometimes used to help further regulate supplies. Experience of cultivars and local conditions is useful but most traditional systems of crop scheduling are imprecise and usually result in peaks and troughs of production. Maintenance of a base level of production by these systems always leads to wasteful, uneconomic or embarrassing over-supply at certain times of the season.

Programmed production related to physical or climatic factors would be preferable but it is more difficult with some crops than others. The problems with cauliflower have been mentioned and the current method of maintaining continuity of supply involves sowing or planting a range of cultivars on a sequence of dates. Correct choice of cultivars and dates needs careful planning since they vary with location and type of cauliflower. Attempts to control maturation by relating sowing dates to prevailing temperatures have failed but it may be possible to use accumulated day-degree intervals to determine more accurate sowing frequencies, (Salter and Laflin, 1974). Salter (1972) has also suggested a continually adjustable drilling schedule using a number of cultivars which mature in a predictable order. Seasonal variations are overcome by including or omitting cultivars with different maturation characteristics.

Scheduling crop development has been more successful with seeding and fruiting vegetables. Vining pea development can be related to day-degree or heat-unit accumulation during the sowing period (Ministry of Agriculture, Fisheries and Food, 1969). A base temperature of 4.5°C is used and successive sowings are made after intervals of the appropriate number of day-degrees. Crop development is slow during periods of low temperature but so is day-degree accumulation and the intervals between sowings are longer than at high temperatures.

The predetermined intervals between sowings are related to average day-degree accumulation figures and to the quantity of peas that factories can accept each day at harvest. There are seasonal variations in cultivar response and it seems that soil temperature may be a better factor than air temperature on which to base accumulated day-degree calculations for peas.

Warnock and Isaacs (1969) suggested a linear heat-unit system using a 6°C base to schedule the development of processing tomato crops in California. They reported close correlations between heat-unit intervals at sowing with scheduled harvest dates. Using processing tomatoes in Portugal, Stilwell and Portas (1978) found no predictable relationship between temperature and either emergence rate or the period from emergence to flowering. Factors such as soil type and water availability also affect emergence while the emergence-to-flowering period is related to time rather than temperature. The 6°C base heat-unit accumulation between seedling emergence and harvest was sufficiently uniform to allow harvest dates to be predicted with reasonable accuracy but there are indications that a system based on a 10°C base temperature would provide greater accuracy. Considerable cultivar variation occurs and it is necessary to determine appropriate intervals for each cultivar and location.

Seeding rate calculations

Researchers demonstrate the plant populations and arrangements necessary to produce vegetables with specific dimensions for particular markets but the introduction of new cultivars, different cultural techniques and harvesting methods may lead to changes in plant density recommendations. Market requirements may change and necessitate plant spacing alterations. Table 5.1 shows spacings and plant densities currently recommended in Britain for a range of vegetables.

Having decided on the appropriate plant density required, seeding rates can then be estimated using the following formula:

$$\text{Weight of seed required (kg/ha)} = \frac{\text{Number of plants required per sq. m} \times 1000}{\text{No. of seeds per g} \times \% \text{ laboratory germination} \times \text{field factor}}$$

Table 5.1   Spacings and plant densities for vegetables

Crop	Row spacing	Plant spacing	Plant density (Number per sq. m)
	Spacings		
Broad bean	45 cm	10–15 cm	21.5–14.0
Dwarf French bean	40 cm	6 cm	43
Pea			
vining	20 cm	5 cm	97
dried	20 cm	7.5 cm	65
market picking	60 cm	7.5 cm	21.5
Beetroot			
early bunching	38 cm	2.5 cm	107
processing	4 rows 5 cm apart at 50 cm centres	5 cm	161
Brussels sprouts			
freezing	45–53 cm	45–53 cm	4.7, 3.5
pre-packing	50–60 cm	50–60 cm	3.9, 2.7
fresh market	60–75 cm	60–75 cm	2.7, 1.7

| Crop | Spacings | | Plant density (Number per sq. m) |
	Row spacing	Plant spacing	
Cabbage			
spring greens	38 cm	7.5–10 cm	34.4–25.8
spring cabbage	40 cm	25 cm	9.7
summer	38 cm	30 cm	8.6
autumn/winter	60 cm	40–60 cm	4.3–2.7
Carrot			
market	10 cm between twin rows at 50 cm centres	3.5 cm	107
dicing	38 cm	5 cm	54
canning	3 rows 2.5 cm apart at 50 cm centres	2.75 cm	377
pre-packing	5 cm between twin rows at 45 cm centres	2.75 cm	161
Cauliflower			
summer	60 cm	45 cm	3.5
autumn/winter	60–70 cm	60–70 cm	2.7–1.9
Celery			
self blanching	25 cm	25 cm	15
main crop	137 cm	15 cm	4.7
Leek			
pre-packing	45 cm	10 cm	21.5
fresh market	45 cm	15 cm	14.3
Lettuce			
Butterheads	30 cm	25 cm	12.9
Crisps	35 cm	30 cm	9.1
Marrows/courgettes			
early	50 cm	50 cm	3.9
maincrop	90 cm	75 cm	1.4
Onion			
spring sown bulb	38 cm	4 cm	65
autumn sown bulb	5 cm between twin rows at 45 cm centres	5 cm	86
salad/bunching	30 cm	0.75–1.25 cm	377–270
pickling	3 rows 2.5 cm apart at 30 cm centres	3.5 cm	270
Parsnip			
pre-packing	40 cm	6 cm	37.6
fresh market	40 cm	7.5–10 cm	32–24
Radish	24 rows 5 cm apart at 150 cm centres	1.6 cm	968
Spinach			
processing	6 rows 20 cm apart at 142 cm centres	1.3 cm	323
fresh market	30 cm	3 cm	107
Sweet corn	60 cm	45 cm	3.5
Turnip	38 cm	7.5 cm	34

(Source: Biggs, 1978)

Seed count and laboratory germination must relate to the particular seed lot. Seed merchants should supply the specific information on request and average figures should never be used since considerable variations are possible. A percentage of the seed which germinates in a laboratory will fail to emerge in the field and the 'field factor' is used to account for the discrepancy. A factor of 0.4 may be used when sowing takes place in poor soil and climatic conditions while a figure of 0.8 is probably the highest that can be achieved. Experience and knowledge of local conditions will influence the choice of field factor but inaccuracies can occur and it has been suggested (Bleasdale, 1973) that it should be omitted from the calculations and the necessary adjustment made by subtracting a constant percentage from the laboratory germination of each crop.

Suppose fresh market carrots are to be grown at 108 per m², there are 950 seeds per g, the laboratory germination of the sample is 85% and a field factor of 0.7 is to be used:

$$\text{Weight of seed required (kg/ha)} = \frac{108 \times 1000}{950 \times 85 \times 0.7} = 1.91 \text{ kg/ha.}$$

Having decided upon an appropriate plant population and calculated the quantity of seed required to sow a given area it may be necessary to know how many seeds should be sown per unit length of row. The following formula provides the information:

$$\text{Number of seeds per metre} = \frac{\text{Average row spacing} \times \text{no. of plants required per sq. m (cm)}}{\text{Percentage laboratory germination} \times \text{field factor}}$$

Using the same example as above but assuming the rows are to be 20 cm apart:

$$\text{Number of seeds per metre} = \frac{20 \times 108}{85 \times 0.7} = 36$$

The calculations must be adjusted for multi-germ beetroot where fruits rather than individual seeds are sown. Each fruit contains several seeds within a corky protective coat. It is necessary to know the number of fruits or clusters per gram and the number of plants produced from 100 clusters. Once again the figures must relate to the particular seed lot to be sown. The seed rate formula is then:

$$\text{Weight per ha} = \frac{\text{No. of plants required per sq. m} \times 1000}{\text{No. of clusters per g} \times \text{no. of plants per 100 clusters} \times \text{field factor}}$$

A similar adjustment is needed in the formula for the number of seeds per metre run with the figure for the number of plants per 100 clusters replacing that for percentage laboratory germination.

The seed rate calculations apply to crops which are grown on overall cropped fields rather than on bed systems which may reduce the total number of rows per hectare and require compensating adjustments to be made.

The influence of soil factors on sowing and emergence

Soil factors which influence sowing, germination and emergence include temperature, moisture levels, soil type and tilth, method of seedbed preparation, depth of sowing, fertiliser ion concentrations and tendency to surface capping. The tendency is for more vegetables to be direct seeded to a stand and it is important to understand these soil factors and their influence on seedling emergence and ultimate plant stand. The 'field factor' represents an attempt to integrate these factors but variations and interactions can be so great that alternative methods of modifying seed rates have been investigated.

Temperature
Optimum temperatures for vegetable seed germiantion have been cited and sowing schedules for processing crops of peas and tomatoes may be based on soil or air temperatures. Hegarty (1976) was unable to relate soil temperature to final percentage seedling emergence, particularly with high vigour seed. Temperature records are therefore of little value to growers who wish to predict final plant stand. The rate at which seedlings emerge is very temperature dependent, however, and increases for many crops up to 20°C provided other factors, such as moisture, are not limiting. Carrots in Britain will take up to six weeks to emerge from March (early spring) sowings but only ten days in July (mid-summer). Germination and emergence of lettuce and onions are reduced by high temperatures whereas beans, tomatoes and cucurbits are affected in a similar way by low temperatures.

Moisture
Water is essential for seed germination but usually has less influence on subsequent seedling emergence. Seed with poor vigour is worst affected by moisture stress and by all other stress factors. Soil moisture effects are less obvious than those of soil temperature but

moisture stress aggravates temperature deficiencies. Seedling emergence can be reduced as much by excessive soil moisture as by shortages. Crops vary in response to moisture and temperature. Brassicas, for example, will succeed in drier, cooler soils than carrots (Hegarty, 1978), and beetroot is more severely affected than most vegetables by moisture stress conditions. Plentiful soil moisture is required to reduce the damaging effects of excessive fertiliser in seedbeds and the use of excessive nitrogenous fertilisers should be avoided.

Seedbed preparation

Ideal seedbeds, provide good contact between seeds and soil, provide minimum resistance to shoot and root growth, allow rapid penetration and retention of water, contain sufficient air and permit uninterrupted gaseous exchange with the atmosphere and resist erosion or loss of structure during rainfall and irrigation. Hegarty (1978) maintains that the ideal tilth would have 50% of the particles with diameters less than 3.0–4.0 mm and have the larger particles near the surface to withstand the impact of rain or irrigation water droplets. These desirable features are most commonly found in loams or other mixed particle sized soils while seedbed preparation is particularly difficult on silts or clays where there is a predominance of small particles.

Great care is required to produce the ideal seedbed and it is particularly important to use the minimum number of cultivations in their preparation. Moisture loss and the likelihood of structural damage increase when soils are over-cultivated. Seedbeds which are prepared immediately before sowing, especially if soil conditions have necessitated the preparations to be forced, are usually less stable than those prepared well in advance of sowing. Seedbeds prepared on poorly structured soils present severe problems since they often collapse or 'slump' when heavy rain or irrigation follows preparation. Violent cultivations often produce fine, 'fluffy' seedbeds which cap in wet weather or blow away in windy conditions. Chemicals may be used to stabilise the soil surface and seedbeds can also be consolidated by rolling. This helps with moisture retention but must be done carefully since smooth soil surfaces will cap easily and impede seedling emergence. The use of sectional ring rollers reduces the likelihood of surface sealing.

Ideally, a seedbed would be prepared with one further cultivation on the primary cultivated surface but conditions are rarely sufficiently favourable. The best time to cultivate is as the soil surface dries out and begins to crumble. Vertical-tine harrows are often used in seedbed preparation but gradual, lateral stirring of the soil with reciprocating or rotary power harrows often produces a firmer stable and graded tilth. A crumbler bar or roller behind the harrow breaks up any final lumps and leaves a level surface.

Great problems can occur when seedbeds must be prepared at regular intervals for successive, intensive crops during dry summer conditions. Over-use of rotavators at high speeds in such conditions soon pulverises soil particles and destroys soil structure.

'Stale' seedbeds are those prepared well in advance of sowing. The first flush of weed seedlings emerges and crops are sown through the weed canopy with the minimum of soil disturbance. Weeds are then immediately sprayed with a suitable contact herbicide so that crop seedlings can emerge into a weed free environment. Moisture is conserved in the seedbed provided cultivations are minimised and sowing is done with very little soil disturbance.

The problem of soil capping referred to in chapter 2 can be a major factor preventing the emergence and growth of seedlings (Royle and Hegarty, 1977). Seedbeds with fine particles on the surface are most likely to cap when heavy rain or irrigation occurs soon after sowing. Chemicals or peat can be applied to stabilise or protect the soil surface while seedling emergence in capped soils is improved by keeping the surface constantly moist by frequent, but light, irrigation.

Before discussing the mechanics of achieving the required seed spacing it is necessary to consider the significance of sowing depth. Control of sowing depth is an important mechanisation factor since uneven depths cause erratic seedling emergence and crop growth. It is particularly important to ensure that all the seeding units on multi-unit drills are operating at the same depth. The effects of sowing depth vary with vegetable species, soil temperatures, soil type and seed size. Large seeds generally emerge better from greater depths than small ones. Deep sowing of large-seeded crops can be used as a safety precaution prior to using residual herbicides. Broad bean seeds can, for example, be sown 5.0–7.5 cm deep in order to reduce the damage risks associated with the use of pre-emergence simazine sprays. Very shallow (1.0 cm) sowings often produce variable emergence since there tend to be fluctuating moisture conditions near the soil surface. Somewhat deeper sowings are preferable especially in dry conditions and Heydecker (1956) recorded a depth of 1.5–2.5 cm to be satisfactory for all but the large seeded vegetables. Sowing at the optimum depth does not always result in a regular stand of seedlings, however, because factors such as seed vigour, soil type and post-sowing conditions may be of overriding importance. Increasing the sowing depth produces a gradual reduction in emergence but again there are crop variations and deeper than optimum sowings of onions perform well in high temperatures although the bulbs form partially below ground and may be more difficult to dry. Shallower than optimum sowing depths produce marked reductions in seedling emergence.

Vegetable seeds used to be broadcast and then the seedlings were thinned to the required spacings. Crops are now grown in rows with the within-row spacings depending on seed, type of drill and required plant population. Vegetables can be divided into two main groups in terms of their spacing requirements; those that are fairly widely spaced (25 cm or more) in each direction such as the brassicas, cucurbits, tomatoes and lettuce and others that are grown much closer together, at least within the rows. This second group includes carrots, beetroot, radish and onions.

The earliest seed drills had no spacing mechanism and metering was by gravity but more sophisticated equipment is now available for precision sowing. Non-spacing drills result in thick-line or thin-line stands of plants and special coulters can be fitted to non-spacing drills when sowing carrots for processing in order to spread out the seed into a scatter band pattern. The difference between thick-line and thin-line drilling is indefinable but before precision drills were available it was standard practice to sow in unspaced lines and remove unwanted seedlings to give the desired spacing. Thinning may still be done either by hand or with machines and has the advantage that weeds can be removed along with unwanted crop seedlings. The system is wasteful of seed, however, and is also labour intensive. Overcrowding often occurs and produces leggy plants which suffer severe competition and susceptibility to disease. Timeliness of thinning, if required, is vital. Radish, salad onions and closely spaced carrots or beetroot for processing are sown this way with no subsequent thinning.

Ideally, precision drilling would consist of sowing a single seed where each plant is required but this is not yet possible. Apart from the mechanical problems created by the size and shape of different seeds there are also the physiological aspects of viability and vigour which can have a major influence on the outcome of the sowing pattern. Various approaches to overcoming such problems were discussed in the previous chapter. Most spacing drills are only accurate with uniformly sized and shaped seeds so graded or pelleted seed is usually required, especially for small seeded crops. Most pellets are uniformly shaped and can be sown at regular spacings with precision drills. The stand of emerged seedlings will not be even, however, unless the necessary number of pellets produce plants. Pelleted seed loses viability more rapidly than natural seed and should not be stored from year to year. Quite a lot of soil moisture is needed to soften the pellets and allow the seeds to germinate. Soils should be adequately moist before sowing although some drills have attachments to water the furrows at sowing time. Irrigation after sowing is less satisfactory because of dangers with soil capping. Pea and sweet corn seeds are large and relatively regularly shaped and can be space sown without any prior size-grading or treatment and there is very little danger of more than one seed being picked up by the selector mechanism. Seeding patterns are based on either uniform spacing or group sowing and vary with the crop, likely seed performance and type of drill. Alternative patterns to achieve a final within the row spacing of 30 cm are shown in fig. 5.1 and the effects of subsequent thinnings on the target population are also demonstrated. Between three and five seeds will be sown for each plant that finally establishes but with group sowing the number of seeds per group should be related to percentage laboratory germination. Three seeds per group should be sufficient when samples have good laboratory germination (above 85%) but there should be 5 or 6 when germination falls below 80%. Vacuum drills can also be used for space sowing and are able to cope with large seeds such as broad beans, marrows and French beans as well as those which are small and irregularly shaped, for example lettuce, carrot and parsnip. Other approaches to precision sowing include the use of taped seeds and the use of fluid drilling although the technology of neither process has yet reached the stage of widespread commercial acceptability. More information on types of drill is given in chapter 11.

No drill, however well designed, can be expected to achieve the correct sowing pattern unless it is carefully calibrated and it is vital that seed drills are calibrated accurately and checked regularly for uniform working. Non-precision drills can produce very acceptable results, especially with closely spaced crops such as bunching carrots or radish, if care is taken with calibration. All the units in a drilling rig must be carefully set for seed delivery and sowing depth. Some spacing drills have electronic safety mechanisms which indicate when particular units are not functioning.

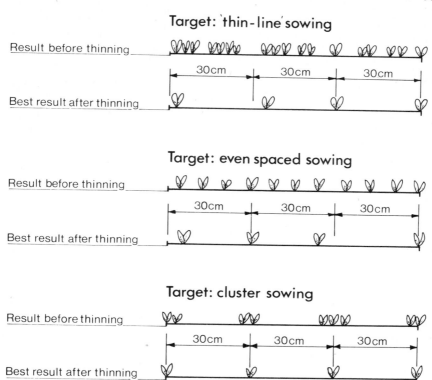

Fig. 5.1. Methods of achieving final spacing and effects of thinning on target populations.

Crop thinning

Unwanted seedlings must be removed at the earliest possible stage to minimise competition. Large numbers of seedlings may have to be removed when crops are sown with non-spacing drills. This is wasteful of seed, tedious and time-consuming but weeds will also be removed at the same time. Small areas may be thinned by hand or with hoes and this also occurs in locations where labour is readily available and cheap. Quite large areas of sugar beet were hand hoed (singled) in Britain until relatively recently. An additional problem with this agricultural crop used to be the multi-germ nature of the 'seeds'. Modern mono-germ varieties have eliminated the difficulty and sowing to a stand is now widely practised. Lettuce is probably the main vegetable that is sometimes sown thickly and hand thinned to the required spacing. Hoeing and singling should be done with the minimum soil disturbance and in warm, drying conditions so that unwanted crop seedlings and weeds die quickly.

It is possible to thin crops mechanically but the process is usually slow and accuracy varies with machine type, uniformity of seedling stand, soil conditions, weed populations, etc. Primitive thinning systems involve cross-blocking by driving equipment at right angles across the rows of drilled crops. This thinning equipment is non-sophisticated and consists of cultivating tines on a tool-bar. Unwanted seedlings are chopped out leaving clumps of crop plants at each station. Hand thinning is then required to produce a completely singled crop. Cross-blocking is not suitable for use on bed systems. Down-the-row thinners usually operate with sharpened blades oscillating or swinging at pre-set intervals across the drilled rows of seedlings. Seedling populations (plants per unit row length) are first estimated to determine thinning intervals. This system is non-selective but works well when there are uniform seedling populations. Difficulties arise when seedling densities vary considerably in the same area. Selective thinning is more sophisticated and can thin crops very accurately in ideal conditions. A sensing device detects plants along the row and transmits the information to a pre-programmed control box. The thinning mechanism is activated at the appropriate intervals and removes unwanted plants. Thinning is usually done mechanically but there are possibilities for chemical removal of unwanted seedlings. Signals from the control box activate spray nozzles which deliver bursts of a contact herbicide such as paraquat. Herbicide drifting is a problem in windy conditions. Mechanical and chemical thinning are more difficult when weeds are growing amongst the crop seedlings as sensing devices cannot distinguish between crop and weeds while dense growths of seedlings are much more difficult to thin accurately. Efficient thinning is most likely when crop seedlings are growing no closer than 5.0–7.5 cm apart in a weed-free seedbed. Soil conditions and tine sharpness must enable unwanted seedlings to be severed cleanly from their roots. Thinners do not work efficiently in wet soils because the seedlings are pulled sideways and re-root rather than being cut off.

Raising plants for transplanting

As an alternative to direct seeding, young plants can be raised, either as so called bare-root transplants or alternatively in various types of containers or modules, for subsequnt planting into their final position in the field. Vegetable growers often raise their own transplants but there are also specialist plant raisers in many areas. Transplant production is an associated part of cauliflower and Brussels sprout culture in important growing areas such as Eastern England and the Vale of Evesham. Celery, which is difficult to establish accurately by direct seeding, is usually transplanted from young plants produced under contract. Raising vegetable plants in peat blocks and various modular systems is also a specialist, factory-style operation utilising, for example, block making machines, sowing attachments which handle natural, pelleted or germinated seed, plant growing houses and well organised delivery services.

Specialist plant raisers may offer for sale a wide range of cultivars within a number of vegetable species or may grow plants under contract for particular farmers and growers. Plant raisers usually supply the seed but occasionally it is provided, such as when the finished crop is grown for processors who have plant breeders to produce their own cultivars. Contracts must be carefully arranged since difficulties may arise over the timing of plant deliveries or collections. Farmers and growers will not want their plants until the soil and weather conditions are suitable but plant raisers cannot delay supply because their growing areas may be needed for other purposes. Cold storing plants or the use of growth-suppressing compounds provide plant raisers and farmers with increased flexibility. Specialist plant raisers use their facilities to produce plants on a continuous basis as is illustrated by producers of lettuce plants in peat blocks. Raisers of other plants, such as cauliflowers or Brussels sprouts, often use their growing areas to produce vegetable plants for part of the year and subsequently grow other crops to fill in periods when there is no demand for plants.

Open ground seedbeds
Brussels sprout, cauliflower, cabbage and leek plants are most commonly raised outdoors. It is important to produce healthy, uniformly sized plants which can be lifted at one time. Sowings must be correctly timed so that transplants are the right size and establish rapidly.

Seedbeds should be prepared well before sowing and have a naturally firm, level and graded tilth. Bed systems are used to minimise compaction in the growing area. Fungal, bacterial or viral diseases may spread from mature crops to young seedlings and seedbed isolation is important. Viruses such as cauliflower mosaic are easily aphid-spread and regular spraying is also important.

Provision of wind break or sun scorch shelters, irrigation facilities and vermin-scaring devices may be necessary while the soil must be pest- and disease-free. Chemical sterilisation of soils with methyl bromide or dazomet will help control soil-borne diseases such as *Rhizoctonia* and *Pythium* and also prevent weed seed germination. Better plant root systems develop when seedbed soils are improved by the addition of peat or other ameliorating organic materials.

Phosphorus is the most important seedling nutrient and nitrogen levels must be kept low until after emergence. Seeds or seedbeds should be treated with appropriate pest or disease control chemicals before sowing. Seedbed spacings influence seedling development, disease incidence, subsequent transplant establishment and crop growth and yield. Overcrowding causes problems and it is much better to space sow graded seed. Williams (1967) and Salter and Fradgley (1969) reported delayed maturity, protracted cutting periods and reduced yields of cauliflower with increasing plant competition in the seedbed. Early transplanting (after 8 weeks rather than 10) from uncrowded seedbeds gave the best yields. Maturity delays were greatest when over-crowded seedlings were kept too long in the seedbed. Rows of brassica plants are usually sown 30 cm apart with seedlings ideally 1.25 cm apart in the rows. This gives a population of approximately 250 plants per m^2. Better plants result if row spacings are reduced and plant spacings widened to give a lower rectangularity. The plant population should not be increased otherwise poor yielding, small transplants are produced. Narrow row spacings are only feasible if weed control can be guaranteed with herbicides or soil sterilant chemicals. Wide spacings must be retained if mechanical weed control is likely.

Leek seedlings are more upright and can be grown closer together. Row spacings of 30 cm are commonly used but space sowing should aim to produce plants at 6 mm intervals. These spacings produce a plant population of 550 per m^2.

Table 5.2 shows the areas that can be planted from different seedbed populations. If, for example, brassica plants are produced at a target population in the seedbed of 250 plants per m^2 (2.5 million per ha) of which only 70% are suitable for transplanting (1.75 million) and a final plant spacing of 60 cm $\times$ 60 cm (27 000 per ha) is required then the table shows that 65 ha can be planted from 1 ha of seedbed.

Weed control is particularly important for crops such as leeks where germination and early growth are very slow. Weed competition at this stage causes severe plant losses. Growth rate is almost

Table 5.2 Plantable areas from different seedbed populations

Seedbed populations (plants per m^2)	250			400			550		
Plant number per ha of seedbed (millions)	2.5			4.0			5.5		
Assume % suitable plants is:	80	70	60	80	70	60	80	70	60
Number usable: (millions)	2.0	1.75	1.5	3.2	2.8	2.4	4.4	3.85	3.3
Plantable area (ha) with final plant population of:									
17 000 per ha (90 cm × 90 cm)	118	103	88	188	165	141	259	226	194
27 000 per ha (60 cm × 60 cm)	74	65	55	118	104	89	163	143	122
47 000 per ha (45 cm × 45 cm)	42.5	37	32	68	59.5	51	94	82	70
108 000 per ha (30 cm × 30 cm)	18.5	16	14	30	26	22	41	35.6	30.5
320 000 per ha (10 cm × 30 cm)	6.25	5.5	4.7	10	8.8	7.5	13.7	12	10.3

impossible to control in outdoor seedbeds and this may be a severe problem when transplanting is delayed by poor weather or slow maturation of previous crops. If plants become too large they are difficult to handle on transplanting machines and establishment losses are increased. Cauliflower growers on the Isle of Thanet, Kent, in Britain, use a rotary cutter to mow off the tops of plants which become too tall in the seedbed and, in really difficult seasons, may do this several times.

Plant raising under protection
More precision and control are possible when plants are raised under protection. The simplest method involves sowing into the soil, often called border soil, under a protective structure. More sophisticated and expensive methods involve the use of seed trays or individual containers such as pots and soil or peat blocks. Plants may be direct sown into individual containers or they may be pricked out from a seed tray or seedbed.

Various types of protective structure are used depending on location, season and type of transplant required. In Britain plants of cabbage, celery or lettuce for very early planting are raised in heated glasshouses. Early maturing cauliflower and Brussels sprout plants are grown in either slightly heated or cold houses while plants for later plantings are raised in unheated structures. Plastic-covered houses are suitable for unheated plant raising and frames or cloches are useful for producing small quantities of transplants. Lathe houses and various kinds of shade houses provide sufficient protection for plant raising in warm climates. Mobile glasshouses are ideal for plant raising since they can be moved off the plants so that growth can be slowed down and they also allow plants to be acclimatised (hardened off) before planting.

Raising plants in the border soil is simply a variation on outdoor seedbeds but the extra environmental control allows more precise production. Specialist plant raisers use the same ground area continually and partial soil sterilisation is necessary to avoid pest and disease build-up. Methyl bromide and dazomet are the most commonly used sterilants and they also give good weed control. Peat or other soil improving materials are added regularly to improve the rooting medium. Fertilisers are applied and incorporated immediately before sowing according to soil analysis. Border plants raised in cool or cold structures during winter should receive very little pre-sowing nitrogen. Top dressings or foliar feeds should be used to apply nitrogen when rapid growth commences.

The border soil is cultivated, firmed if necessary and raked into a fine, level tilth before sowing. It used to be common practice to broadcast seed evenly onto the prepared surface and then lightly rake it in but efficient broadcasting requires a lot of skill and now specialist spacing drills are used. Several types of drill are available, some of which have been designed specifically to sow individual seeds very close together in narrow rows. Brassica seeds are sown 2.5 cm apart in rows 7.5 cm apart. This gives a theoretical population of 533 plants per m^2 although 400 per m^2 is considered preferable if space is available. Size graded seed may be needed to ensure that only one seed is dropped at each position. F_1 hybrid brassica seed is often more uniformly sized than that of open-pollinated varieties, in which case natural seed may provide sufficient accuracy. Graded seed costs at least twice as much as ungraded. Very close spacings increase the likelihood of attack by damping-off fungi (*Rhizoctonia* and *Pythium*) and downy mildews.

Weeds must be controlled chemically if very close spacings are to be used. Regular soil sterilisation will reduce weed populations but deep cultivations bring unaffected seeds to the surface and some soil improving materials may contain considerable quantities of weed seeds.

All the plants are cleared in one go with workers 'pulling' or 'drawing' them from the seedbed and bundling them for easy handling during transplanting. Such plants are sometimes known as 'pulled' or 'drawn' plants. Growth control is difficult especially when plants are grown in unheated, static structures. Specialist plant raisers must make maximum use of their protective structures and it is important to change over quickly between one crop of plants and the next.

Raising in containers or blocks
Plants raised in containers or blocks are usually grown in specially prepared growing media. Many different media (composts) are available but there is an increasing use of soil-less media based on peat, sand, grit, vermiculite, perlite, polystyrene or other materials.

Container-raised plants are relatively expensive to produce and must have compensatory advantages over plants grown in border soil or outdoor seedbeds. They may be bigger plants, more uniformly developed and have the potential for rapid establishment in the field. Root disturbance and damage at transplanting is less than with bare-root plants so that establishment and regrowth should be quicker. Larger volumes of compost per plant usually improve subsequent development and establishment in the field but large root balls present particular difficulties during machine planting. Large containers occupy more plant raising space and it is important that final crop returns justify the additional plant raising costs. Crops grown on intensively cultivated holdings for the very earliest markets may be raised in this way. Examples in Britain include very early summer cauliflower, protected runner beans and some outdoor tomatoes.

Containers may be direct-seeded or seedlings can be raised in seed trays or the glasshouse border soil before being pricked out into the containers. Pricking out allows seed germination and early development to take place in small isolated areas so that space is conserved and specialist facilities, such as additional heating or misting lines, are used most efficiently. Celery seed germinates very well on the surface of media placed under misting lines at temperatures of 13–18°C. The seedlings are then pricked out into containers and grown on at 15°C. Direct-seeding saves time, labour and seed but uses more space for longer periods of time and may not be particularly suitable for some crops. Plants must develop in a very high percentage of the containers and sowing two seeds per container may improve the percentage but additional labour is then needed for the thinning that will be required. Lettuce, celery, celeriac and brassica seed are small and difficult to sow singly into containers by hand. Vacuum seeding equipment overcomes some of the problems with individual seeds being sucked against holes at predetermined spacings in metal or plastic plates. The plate is then held over the containers and the vacuum released to free the seeds. Problems with picking up more than one seed are reduced when pelleted seeds are used. Some of the split-pill pellets are particularly suitable for direct seeding. Other equipment is available for sowing natural or pelleted seeds into peat blocks, pots, seed trays or paper pot systems.

Misses still occur but the risk is minimised when pre-germinated seeds are direct sown. Sweet corn, melons, courgettes (zucchini) and legumes have large seeds which can be germinated and then direct sown into containers by hand. This is laborious on anything but a very small scale and automatic devices are now available which inject germinated seeds in a protective gel into blocks, pots or containers. The system has great potential for incorporating fertilisers, fungicides, insecticides, etc., into the gel to provide an ideal environment for seedling development.

Vegetable plants are now rarely raised in clay pots although plastic ones are occasionally used. Plants must be knocked out of the containers before planting and pots must be collected again afterwards. This is consequently a labour intensive system but may be justified on small, hand-planted areas where the potential returns are high. Pots made from compressed peat, or various types of treated paper allow roots to come through and are planted with the plant. Root emergence out of the pot is hindered when the peat or paper dries out and the whole pot must be completely buried to prevent drying out after planting. Slitting the pot wall before planting reduces the root emergence problem. The Japanese devised a paper pot system for raising sugar beet plants which has since been adopted for vegetable production. The pots are bottomless, cylindrical or hexagonal in shape and joined together into long honeycombs which are stretched out and filled with compost. They can then be direct seeded or seedlings can be pricked out into the pots. Individual pots are stuck together with water-soluble glue which dissolves during plant raising to leave separate units.

Vegetable plants are grown in seed trays (flats) of different sizes and may be direct sown or pricked out. Trays are often constructed from lightweight materials like plastic or polystyrene and may be divided into compartments so that roots do not become interwoven and damaged when plants are removed. Plant populations and spacings vary with the vegetable species and local traditions. A typical seed tray measures 35 cm × 22 cm and is used for between 30 and 60 vegetable plants. Overcrowding must be avoided or weak, spindly plants are produced which are disease-prone and establish very badly.

Peat and soil blocks are planted with the seedlings and large quantities of growing medium are added to the outside land during planting. This can markedly improve soil conditions particularly with closely spaced, intensively grown vegetables such as lettuce where three or four crops may be planted and grown on the same site each year. There are dangers, however, if bought-in or home-produced blocks contain persistent and damaging pests or diseases. Club root of brassicas (*Plasmodiophora brassicae*) and white rot of onions (*Sclerotium cepivorum*) are potential problems along with big vein virus of lettuce which is transmitted by the fungus *Olpidium*. Block planting of lettuce has increased rapidly during recent years in Britain with a lot of plants coming from specialist plant raisers. Big vein virus is difficult to eradicate from plant raising nurseries and from lettuce growing fields.

Block size does not appear to influence plant establishment and subsequent growth or yield but there could be important economic considerations. Most crops are raised in 3.8–4.5 cm cuboid blocks but it may be worth using larger blocks (6.0 cm) in order to put out more advanced plants of potentially valuable crops. McKee (1978) and Cox *et al.* (1979) have shown that soils in Britain are often very dry in the top 8 cm when transplanting takes place in spring or early summer. Short, squat blocks (2.5 cm deep) are very stable and unlikely to fall over during transplanting but plant establishment is poor since the roots have difficulty in reaching down to moist soil. Long, narrow blocks however, establish more rapidly because roots emerge directly into wet soil. Block stability during transplanting is improved when long, conical blocks are used (2 cm upper diameter/5 cm basal diameter).

Equipment is available which stamps out blocks and delivers a natural, pelleted or germinated seed into each one. High temperature dormancy problems occur when using dry lettuce seed at temperatures above 25°C but seeded blocks can be stacked for the first 24 hours in a cool building or alternatively placed on thoroughly moistened ground and covered with 2.5 cm thick insulating sheets of polystyrene. Lettuce seedling growth is rapid at high temperatures after germination.

Blocking media can be impregnated with some crop protection chemicals to give long-term pest or disease control.

There is usually one plant to every block and the cost of planting closely spaced crops can be very high at usual spacings. Plant costs are reduced if more than one plant is grown in each block and multi-seeded blocks have proved successful for bulb onions, salad onions and calabrese. Traditionally these crops are direct seeded in the field. Transplanting allows them to be grown in less favourable areas and multi-seeded blocks could reduce the plant costs. Six to twelve seeds are sown per 4.5 cm block for bulb onions and ten to twelve for salad onions where the whole bunch of mature plants is pulled during harvesting.

There are many methods of raising vegetable plants but the transplanting operation still requires considerable labour inputs. The majority of plants are transplanted with hand-fed machines but automatic planters are being designed. Automated planting requires purpose-produced transplants and development work at the National Institute of Agricultural Engineering, Silsoe, in Britain, has led to the production of strips (bandoliers) of cylindrical blocks. The growing medium is formed into cylinders which are held together by a paper/polythene laminate and direct seeded with natural, pelleted or germinated seeds. Plants develop in the bandoliers which are then fed through automatic planters which chop the strips into individual plant containing units prior to planting.

In recent years there has been a marked increase in the use of modular systems for raising vegetable transplants, particularly when used in conjunction with machine planting (Ministry of Agriculture, Fisheries and Food, 1981). The 'Speedling' system for example uses rigid polystyrene trays consisting of discrete tapered cells (i.e. inverted pyramid in shape) each with an opening at its apex to permit both drainage and air pruning of roots as they emerge from the base of the tray. Plants raised in these trays develop a large quantity of lateral roots which bind the compost within each compartment thus facilitating the removal of the plant with its root system at transplanting.

Many other available systems are based on the multi-celled rigid polystyrene tray principle. The 'Techniculture' transplant system developed in the U.S.A., originally to use in crisp lettuce production, is based on a small cylindrical 'plug' of compost which is rendered robust and flexible by the inclusion of a binding agent.

These and other modular raised transplants are illustrated in fig. 5.2.

Planting

Transplanting allows vegetable seedlings to be raised in isolation where they can be given attention and protection. Crops occupy their final positions for shorter periods and more time is available for clearing the previous crop. Target plant populations are easier to achieve and the plants can be selected and graded before planting.

Growth checks, however, often occur after tansplanting and these must be minimised. Pulling plants from open-ground seedbeds or border soil may cause loss or damage to 25–50% of the root system. The damage is reduced by thoroughly wetting the soil before lifting, undercutting the beds of plants and hand forking plants out of the ground. Container-raised plants suffer less disturbance but, again, plants should always be well watered before transplanting. A much used horticultural practice is to harden-off (pre-condition) plants by withholding water and reducing temperatures before planting in order to minimise transplanting checks. However, recent research (Cox et al., 1979) has shown that successful establishment is linked with moisture stress levels in the transplant and withholding water

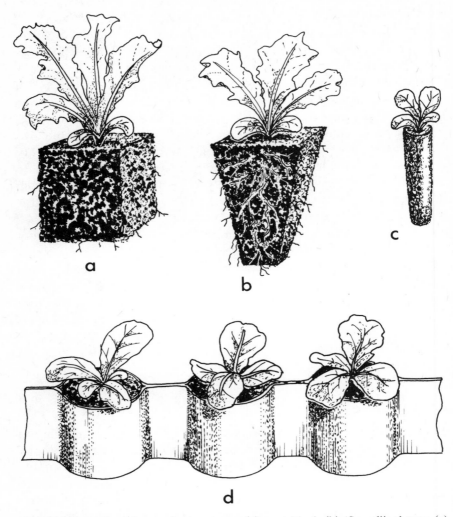

Fig. 5.2. Examples of transplant systems. (a) peat block (b) 'Speedling' type (c) 'Techniculture' plug and (d) 'Bandolier' system.

before planting is deleterious. Root damage to transplanting increases moisture stress and bare-root plants may establish nine or ten days more slowly than container-raised plants. Levels of abscisic acid in the plant increase during moisture stress conditions and, by inducing stomatal closure, help to reduce water loss. It is possible that foliar applications of synthetic anti-transpirant materials can be used to help reduce transplanting checks in a similar way. The moisture status of field soils also affects plant establishment. The best establishment is achieved from planting well watered transplants into moist field conditions, although well watered plants establish better in dry soils than unwatered plants in wet soils. This is particularly important for container-raised plants.

Space sowing into seedbeds or raising plants in containers should result in a high proportion of uniform plants at planting time. There is conflicting evidence on the value of size-grading plants prior to transplanting. Salter and Fradgley (1969) showed few advantages from grading two cultivars of autumn cauliflower but Williams (1967) demonstrated direct correlations between transplant size and both total yield and earliness of harvest of winter cauliflower. Large transplants gave higher and earlier yields. Older plants suffer greater transplanting checks, however, and it is important to find the optimum planting stage. Experience suggests that size-grading is worthwhile, however, to produce more uniformly maturing crops. Large-, medium- and small-sized transplants will all produce reasonable crops in time but irregular maturation is wasteful of land and a particular nuisance if once-over harvesting is planned. Planting large plants separately from the small should allow areas of crop to be cleared in sequence.

Plants should be pulled singly from seedbeds and bundled so that they can be handled easily by operators on the transplanters. Very small, abnormal or diseased plants must be discarded. It is vitally important that soil-borne diseases from the seedbed are not transferred to the growing fields. Abnormalities of plants may include colour variations and stunting as with 'sib' seedlings (sister × brother crosses) of F_1 hybrid Brussels sprouts or plants without growing points (blind) in a number of brassicas.

Some pre-planting chemical treatments are applied immediately prior to transplanting. Seedbeds or individual containers may be watered with insecticides, fungicides or micro-nutrient solutions at this stage. Incorporation of crop protection chemicals into blocking composts has been mentioned already but pre-planting treatments are also possible. Brassica plants can be protected against subsequent attack by cabbage root fly larvae (*Delia radicum*) by watering with a solution of an appropriate insecticide such as chlorfenvinphos. Alternatively the protection can be afforded by dipping the roots of bare-root brassica transplants into protectant chemicals. Protection against club root (*Phasmodiophora brassicae*) is claimed from dipping brassica transplant roots into carbendazim, thiophanate-methyl or mercurous chloride (calomel). 'Whiptail' of cauliflowers reduces the amount of leaf lamina and is caused by molybdenum deficiency (either actual or induced). The problem can be avoided by watering the plants at an early stage with a 0.025% solution of sodium molybdate (100 lit. of solution should treat 300 m^2 of seedbed). If the soil in the final growing positions is likely to induce 'whiptail' then another molybdate watering should be given just before planting.

Weather, soil or other factors often prevent transplanting taking place on schedule and plants must remain longer in seedbeds or containers. It is rarely possible to slow down growth by adjusting environmental factors such as temperature but it may be possible to move plants outside from protected structures or, if movable structures have been used, to move the protection onto another site. Drastic measures such as mowing over the plants are not recommended.

Thomas (1976) has reported that daminozide (B-nine) or chlormequat chloride (Cycocel) can be sprayed onto transplant seedlings to suppress aerial growth and improve root development. Results have been somewhat variable with brassica crops but both chemicals have produced beneficial effects on tomato transplant establishment and subsequent growth. These treatments can be very valuable when applied early in the seedling stage but are unlikely to have the necessary retardation just before lifting and transplanting.

Another possibility for 'holding' plants is to keep them in cold store but, again, results have been variable. Cold storage would have an additional advantage for summer and autumn cauliflower plants which require low temperature treatments for curd initiation. Transplanted crops show much more maturation variability than direct seeded plants and may need harvesting over four-week periods or longer. It appears that the spread of harvest is closely correlated with the length of time taken for curds to be initiated. In practice this can often be a long time especially in variable weather conditions and artificial cooling at the appropriate growth stage may induce more uniform maturation. Curds are initiated when the seedlings are small but the exact stage varies with cultivar and the plants may be anything from six weeks to twelve weeks old. Salter and Ward (1972) gave plants two weeks at 2°C before planting and produced better maturation but not as uniform as the 80% reported from direct drilled crops. Problems occurred when cold treated plants were transplanted during very warm weather and it would be better to plant in cool, humid conditions. Similar pre-planting cold treatment advantages have been reported for tomato (Wiebe and Tiessen, 1964) where flowering has been advanced.

Bare-root plants pose the greatest establishment problems and must be out of the ground for the shortest possible time. Even those plants which are pulled from previously watered seedbeds soon wilt and heat up. Plants should ideally be pulled early in the day before temperatures are too high. After pulling and bundling they should be kept in a cool, shaded place and covered with thoroughly moistened cloth or sacks. Metabolic activity continues and bare-root plants, particularly brassicas, soon heat up and tissue breakdown occurs.

Labour must be well organised at planting if 'waiting time', efficient machine use and plant losses are to be minimised. Work rates of transplanting machine operators are affected by plant spacings, soil conditions, type of transplant, etc., but should be in the range of 1500–2500 plants per hour. Estimates suggest that it takes about 45 man hours to plant a hectare of summer cabbage and 80 man hours for lettuce. Sufficient plant pullers should be employed to maintain the requisite supply of plants to the fields. Automatic planting could reduce the labour problems provided that the systems of plant raising and transplanting are fully integrated. Some of the earliest automatic transplanters used more additional labour to prepare and supply plants to the machine in the required form than was saved by having unmanned machines. More recent systems appear to overcome these difficulties.

Planting methods

Transplanting on a small scale or in areas with skilled, rapid workers may be done by hand. Container-raised vegetables are often planted with trowels and very little transplanting check should occur. There will be the post-planting operation of pot collection when plants are raised in non-plantable containers. Correct depth of planting and crop spacing are relatively easily achieved with hand planting in well prepared, previously-worked land but rapid work rates are difficult to maintain. For this reason almost all transplanting of vegetables is now carried out either with machine assistance or by fully automatic planters. For example, mechanical dibbing machines are available to facilitate the hand planting of leeks. These not only speed up the operation but also produce a standard depth planting hole which contributes to a greater uniformity in the harvested crop than can be achieved using other techniques of hand planting. Success of the operation depends very much on having soil at the correct moisture content at the time of dibbing, since soil that is too wet may smear and dry soil will refill the holes.

Other types of machinery range from those that simply open a planting furrow in which plants are placed by hand, through to completely automatic planters where specially designed modular raised transplants are handled entirely mechanically. These are discussed more fully in chapter 11.

Apart from the savings in labour and time that can be achieved with mechanised planting, there are also advantages of uniformity in that spacing and depth of planting can be more precisely controlled. This will contribute towards a more uniform crop at the time of harvesting.

Attachments can be fitted which deliver crop protection chemicals, usually granular insecticides, for incorporation around the roots during transplanting. Watering attachments are also available and can be fitted to individual planting units to deliver a measured dose of water to each plant as it is planted. The watering attachments are fed from tanks which are either mounted to the front of the tractor or fitted as saddles. Some vegetables can be sprayed with herbicide immediately after planting and it is possible to mount the spray boom directly behind the planting units. Multiple operations of this type reduce the passage of equipment over the field and hence minimise soil structure damage.

Post-planting care

Transplanting checks are likely to be reduced if plants are watered in immediately. Watering attachments for planting machines have been mentioned but further waterings may be needed. Spot applications use water more economically than overall sprays and plants should be given between 70 to 140 ml at each watering. Establishment is quicker if starter fertilisers are added to the water. A balanced mixture of major nutrients applied around the plant allows easy uptake by damaged roots. Some transplants will die and crops should be 'gapped up' as soon as possible after planting. Plants should be kept aside for this purpose since a few hours spent at this stage will help to ensure uniform crop maturity at harvest.

Birds and vermin can cause serious damage soon after planting. Some bird species will systematically pull plants out of the ground and leave them on the surface. Firm planting reduces the problem which ceases altogether when new roots form and anchor the plants.

The possibility of using abscisic acid (ABA) as an anti-transpirant has already been referred to, although it appears that any beneficial effect of using this material is more likely to arise from its ability, at least in cauliflowers, to increase the root:shoot ratio (Biddington and Dearman, 1982). A number of other materials exist which have anti-transpirant properties, including metabolic inhibitors such as phenylmercuric acetate (PMA) which are able to promote stomatal closure. Film type materials can also be sprayed on plants to prevent water loss but these appear to be more useful for application on transplanted nursery stock than on vegetable transplants. Although the concept of spraying vegetables with anti-transpirants to improve establishment is attractive, experimental studies in this area have proved disappointing.

Plastic-aided establishment and growth

Polyethylene (polythene) and plastics are used in various ways to allow crops to be sown or planted earlier, to improve and speed up seedling emergence, to protect soil surfaces and to shorten growing seasons or promote crop maturity and they may even make production of some otherwise uneconomic crops a viable prop- osition in latitudes with marginal growing conditions.

Low tunnels (around 60 cm wide and high) made from thin polythene sheet (38μ/150 gauge) supported by wire hoops are used in a number of countries to provide protection and improve environmental conditions for early cold-susceptible vegetables such as lettuce, melons, celery, etc.

Black polythene sheet can be laid onto the soil surface where it acts as a mulch for crops which are sown or planted through it. As with all mulches soil temperatures are higher (by as much as 6–8°C), moisture is conserved and weed growth is suppressed. Mulches are particularly valuable in increasing the speed of emergence of direct seeded crops. Watering is not a problem when narrow width sheets are used since moisture moves laterally from the edges of beds towards the centres. Uninterrupted coverage of large areas with non-perforated polythene will require some kind of drip-irrigation underneath the sheeting. Wide or narrow beds are covered with black sheet for the production of strawberries, lettuce and melons. The sheets are picked (or rolled) up at the end of the season to allow the soil to be cultivated but they may be used again in subsequent years. Alternatively the polythene can be left down and can last for up to three years.

In recent years, intensive vegetable producers in temperate

regions have been turning to the use of floating mulches as a method of improving crop establishment and extending their growing seasons. Floating mulches consist of strips of clear, perforated polythene (slit film) laid over the top of sown or planted crops to provide protection and promote early growth (fig. 5.3). Mulch-laying machines have been specially designed to lay the perforated sheets and bury the edges at the sides of the sown or planted beds. The perforations give the sheets elastic properties so that they are pushed up by developing crops. Gaseous exchange takes place readily and rain or irrigation can penetrate through to the soil. Humidity tends to build up under the sheets while plant growth is soft and can be easily damaged when crops are uncovered during drying conditions. The successful use of this technique hinges on knowing at exactly what stage the plastic should be removed. The material usually lasts through a growing season and must be rewound after use. Machines have been developed to rewind the film.

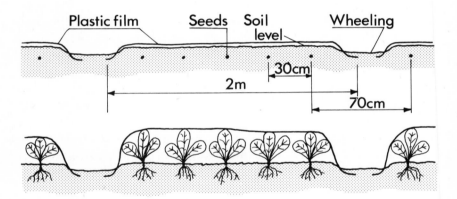

Fig. 5.3. Floating mulch system of crop production

Degradable mulches

Rapidly degrading films break down in one season usually under the agency of bright sunlight. The rate of photodegradation varies depending on light levels and the amount of degradation chemical which the film contains. Life spans range from 30 to about 130 days and the films may be clear or coloured. White and aluminium coloured films may have an additional advantage since reflections from them can deter aphids from landing and inoculating cucurbitous plants with mosaic viruses. Clear materials have the drawback that weed growth is not suppressed although pre-laying herbicide treatments can be used to overcome this problem. The U.S.A., Japan and the Mediterranean countries are major users of photo-degradable mulches especially for solanaceous (tomato, pepper, aubergine) and cucurbitous (melon, cucumber, squash, courgette/zucchini) crops. Machinery has been developed which lays the mulches and allows planting or sowing to take place at the same time.

Strip covers for seedlings

An alternative mulching system has been developed at the Institute of Agricultural Engineering (IMAG), Wageningen, Netherlands. Meijer (1978) reports that 20 cm wide strips of clear polythene are laid over drilled lines immediately after sowing. The edges of the strips are buried to prevent the polythene blowing away. Specially designed machines lay the polythene during sowing and it is also possible to apply herbicides at the same time. Soil temperatures and moisture content are increased below the strips and the soil surface is protected against capping. Seedling emergence can be improved and earlier sowings may be possible. The polythene is left down until seedlings emerge (perhaps ten to twenty days) when hydraulically-powered implements are used to rewind the strips. Thermodormancy problems of lettuce may be aggravated by the higher temperatures produced under the polythene but it seems that this mulching system may be particularly useful for crops such as beetroot, brassicas, chicory, etc., which have strong, broad-leaved seedlings.

References and further reading

Biddington, N.L. and Dearman, A.S. (1982) 'The effect of abscisic acid on root and shoot growth of cauliflower plants'. *Plant Growth Regulators*, **1**, 15–24.

Biggs, A.G. (June, 1978) 'Sowing rates for vegetable seeds'. *Horticultural Industry*, 59.

Bleasdale, J.K.A. (1973) *Plant Physiology in relation to Horticulture*. London: MacMillan.

Cox, E.F., McKee, J.M.T., Dearman, A.S. and Kratky, B.A. (1979) 'Transplant establishment'. *Report of National Vegetable Research Station for 1978*, 97–99.

Eastwood, J. and Gray, D. (1976) 'New systems of establishing field lettuce crops assessed'. *Horticultural Research*, **15**, 65–75.

Gray, D. (1978) 'Comparison of fluid drilling and conventional establishment techniques on seedling emergence and crop uniformity in lettuce'. *Journal of Horticultural Science*, **53**, 23–30.

Heath, J.E. (1978) The timing of outdoor lettuce and comparisons betwen direct drilled and transplanted programmes'. *Acta Horticulturae*, **72**, 179–183.

Hegarty, T.W. (1976) 'Field establishment of some vegetable crops; response to a range of soil conditions'. *Journal of Horticultural Science*, **51**, 133–146.

Hegarty, T.W. (1978) 'Seedbed conditions and seedling establishment'. *Acta Horticulturae*, **83**, 297–307.

Heydecker, W. (1956) 'Establishment of seedlings in the field. I. Influence of sowing depth on seedling emergence'. *Journal of Horticultural Science*, **31**, 76–88.

McKee, J.M.T. (1978). 'The effect of block size and shape'. *Report of National Vegetable Research Station for 1977*, 58.

Meijer, E.N.C. (1978) 'Temporary covering of drilled lines of vegetable crops with transparent polythene film'. *Acta Horticulturae*, **72**, 251–253.

Ministry of Agriculture, Fisheries and Food (1969) *Peas*. Bulletin 81, London: H.M.S.O.

Ministry of Agriculture, Fisheries and Food (1981) *Propagating and Transplanting Vegetables*. Ref. Book 344, London:H.M.S.O.

Rickard, P.C. (1972) 'How to minimise the problem of direct drilled celery'. *Grower*, **7**, 1268–1269.

Royle, S.M. and Hegarty, T.W. (1977) 'Soil impedance and field emergence in calabrese'. *Journal of Horticultural Science*, **52**, 535–543.

Salter, P.J. (1972) 'An adjustable drilling sequence to compensate for adverse weather conditions and to obtain continuous production of vegetable crops'. *Horticultural Research*, **12**, 57–63.

Salter, P.J. and Fradgley, J.R.A. (1969) 'Effects on crop maturation in cauliflower: II. Effects of cultural factors on the maturity characteristics of a cauliflower crop'. *Journal of Horticultural Science*, **44**, 141–154.

Salter, P.J. and Laflin, T. (1974) 'Studies on methods of obtaining continuity of production of summer and autumn cauliflowers. V. The role of short-term storage and conclusions from experiments'. *Experimental Horticulture*, **26**, 120–129.

Salter, P.J and Ward, R.J. (1972) 'Studies on crop maturity in cauliflowers: III. Effects of cold treatment and certain growth regulators on crop maturity characteristics and yield'. *Journal of Horticultural Science*, **47**, 57–68.

Stilwell, M.R. and Portas, C.A. (1978) 'Timing in Portuguese direct seeded tomatoes for industry'. *Acta Horticulturae*, **72**, 201–210.

Thomas, T.H. (1976) 'Growth regulation in vegetable crops'. *Outlook on Agriculture*, **9**, (**2**), 62–68.

Warnock, S.J. and Isaacs, R.L. (1969) 'A linear heat unit system for tomatoes in California'. *Journal American Society of Horticultural Science*, **94**, 677–678.

Wiebe, J. and Tiessen, H. (1964) 'Growing vegetable transplants'. *Publication of Ontario Depratment of Agriculture*, No. 485.

Williams, A.M. (1967) 'Winter cauliflower – seedling densities'. *Report of Rosewarne Experimental Horticultural Station for 1966*, 50–52.

6   Weed, pest and disease control

Previous chapters have dealt with factors leading up to crop establishment. The present chapter surveys the scientific principles underlying modern methods of control of pests affecting vegetables in the field. In this context pests include weeds, a term used for virtually any plant that has a detrimental effect on crop production, animal pests, particularly insects but including most other orders as well, and diseases caused by fungi, bacteria and viruses. These may be responsible for substantial losses and even in the U.S.A., where technological standards are high, average losses of, for example, cabbage have been estimated to be of the order of 20% and tomatoes as high as 30%. In tropical regions the figures are invariably higher and total crop losses are not infrequent. Successful control of any pest problem must be based on a detailed knowledge of the organism's life cycle. The competitive effects of weed growth on vegetable production are less dramatic than a serious insect attack or the outbreak of a disease but, if left unchecked, can also cause the total loss of a crop. It has been said that more energy is expended in the weeding of man's crops than for any other single human task.

Characteristics of weeds

Weeds compete with vegetables for light, water and mineral nutrients. The majority of vegetable crops are grown as annuals in land that is frequently cultivated and in such a situation weeds are characteristically fast growing annuals. Species such as annual meadow grass (*Poa annua*), shepherd's purse (*Capsella bursa-pastoris*), annual nettle (*Urtica dioica*) and chickweed (*Stellaria media*) are important competitors in such situations. Life cycles are short and in warm weather it is frequently no more than six weeks from germination of a weed until flowering. Large numbers of seeds can be produced by a single plant, frequently in excess of 2000, and efficient dispersal mechanisms can guarantee the rapid spread of a weed. Although weeds which primarily reproduce from seed numerically represent the most important species to the grower, there are others such as couch grass (*Agropyron repens*) and creeping thistle (*Cirsium arvense*), which multiply via rhizomes and may represent even more of a problem in certain situations. In this instance the dispersal of the weed is aided by the cultivation of the soil which helps to divide and spread portions of the rhizomes.

Many weed species are able to germinate and grow more rapidly at lower temperatures than the vegetable crop and thus can gain an advantage in time. They start to compete for light early and by shading the developing vegetable crop maintain their advantage.

Many weed species develop deep tap roots at an early stage which puts them at an advantage in their competition for water and nutrients.

Another aspect of the success of weed species is their ability to survive. In contrast to most vegetables which have been selected for uniform and rapid germination the seeds of weeds frequently exhibit some form of dormancy. Mechanical and physiological features frequently combine to ensure that seeds buried by cultivation remain viable for long periods to germinate later when conditions are favourable for growth. The environmental conditions required to trigger germination will vary between species and although some may present a continuing problem throughout the growth of a crop others may be more seasonal in their distribution. For example in temperate regions shepherd's purse will germinate throughout the year whereas redshank (*Polygnum persicaria*) has a main wave of germination in the spring. Other species such as common fumitory (*Fumaria officinalis*) may exhibit two waves of germination in the spring and autumn. A knowledge of weed biology is a necessary prerequisite for planning effective control measures.

Effects of weed growth on production

In addition to the effects of weed competition, there are a number of other problems created by weed growth. Pests and diseases will be discussed in more detail later in this chapter but it is appropriate to mention at this stage that crops weakened by competition from weed growth are more likely to be susceptible to attack. Weeds may also harbour pests and diseases.

Harvesting is made more difficult by the presence of weeds and this becomes more of a problem with harvesting machines which are less able to distinguish between crop and weed than with a human harvesting by hand. The tough wiry stems of species such as knotgrass (*Polygnum aviculare*) can, for example, cause problems in the mechanised harvesting of dwarf beans. The presence of weeds or their seeds is likely to result in downgrading and even rejection of some crops.

Yield losses from competition by weeds is probably the grower's major concern although, of course, the above factors will also play a part in the assessment of the economics of various control strategies. When weed populations are low, yield reduction may be minimal, but a stage is reached when severe competition sets in and yield declines rapidly. A completely clean crop is therefore unlikely to be justified although the critical weed populations at which weed control should be implemented are difficult to predict. The developing pattern of competition between crop and weed is complex and will depend not only on their relative population densities but also on their species composition.

It is unnecessary to keep a crop free of weeds throughout its growing period. If the crop is kept free for a long enough period at the start of its life it may be able to effectively swamp out the effects of later developing weeds. Similarly, provided weeds are removed before effective competition ensues then the presence of weeds during the early stages may have little or no effect on final yields. These contrasting situations are illustrated in fig. 6.1 where it is evident that there is a critical period in the crop development during which weeds must be eliminated if yields are not to suffer. This example is based on weed control in onions (Hewson and Roberts, 1971), although similar principles will apply to other crops. Clearly there are differences between species but this form of analysis illustrates the changing pattern of competition with crop development and highlights the importance of timeliness in weed control measures. Similar studies on beetroot and broad beans (Roberts, 1976) showed that these crops were able to compete more effectively than onions against weed competition. In both instances a single weeding was sufficient to prevent losses in yield although the timing of the operation was more critical for beetroot than for broad beans.

Weed control

Before considering the role of chemicals in the control of weeds it should be noted that herbicides are a relatively recent development. They have done much to replace the mechanical techniques

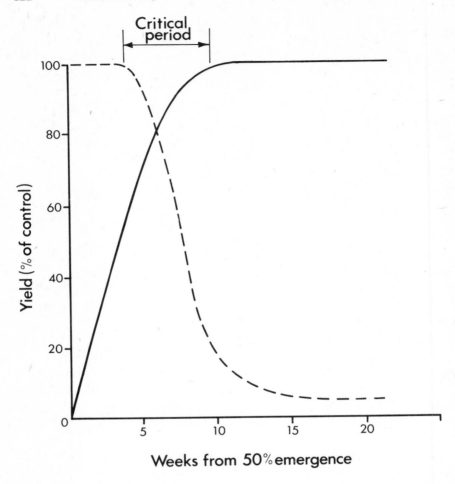

Fig. 6.1. Effect on final yield of allowing weeds to remain for different periods before removal (dotted line) and of preventing weeds from establishing for different periods (solid line) (after Hewson and Roberts, 1971).

although the latter still have an important part to play and are therefore considered before discussing the use of herbicides.

Primary cultivation is still very much based on the mould board plough which serves to bury remaining crop residues and weeds, although of course it also brings buried weed seeds into the surface layers where they will germinate during favourable weather conditions. The subsequent preparation of seedbeds using harrows or cultivators will help to destroy the weed seedlings and also stimulate other weed seeds to germinate. Timely and frequent cultivation at this early stage will help to reduce the weed population, a process which can be continued during the early stages of crop growth using inter-row hoes and cultivators. However, the weed seed population in the top 15 cm of a vegetable field is usually extremely high, (one estimate is in the order of 25 000 per m^2) and it would take many years of regular cultivation during which further flowering and weed seed production is prevented to lower this to an acceptable level at which competition is negligible. In most systems of intensive production it becomes necessary to supplement these mechanical methods with chemical herbicides.

The development of herbicides was slow until about 1950 after which large numbers were introduced at an accelerating rate until by 1980 there were almost one hundred chemicals available in over five hundred different commercial formulations. The choice and use of a suitable herbicide are consequently complex and depend on numerous biological and economic factors in nature.

The first consideration of importance to a grower is whether or not the chemical to be used is *selective* or *non-selective* in its action. *Non-selective* herbicides have a role to play in cleaning uncropped areas but they may also be used selectively by careful inter-row, or directed, spraying between a developing crop, thus preventing the chemical reaching the latter. Clearly a non-selective herbicide used in close proximity to a growing crop, or in areas which are shortly to be cropped must have no residual effects. The chemical paraquat is frequently used for such purposes.

In most instances, however, a grower requires a seletive chemical which will kill the weeds but not the crop. Unfortunately selectivity depends on many factors, some of which are outside the grower's control. They include, for example, the type of chemical, its concentration, the crop, its stage of growth, soil type, weather conditions, soil moisture and temperature, weed species present and their stage of growth.

Herbicides are further classified by both their mode of action and method of application. A chemical can kill on *contact*, only affecting those parts of the plant receiving direct exposure to the chemical, or the chemical may be *translocated* through the vascular system following absorption thus affecting all parts of the plant. These different modes of action affect the manner in which the chemical must be applied since complete coverage is more critical in the case of contact herbicides.

An alternative to spraying chemicals on the crop, i.e. foliar spraying, is to apply a *residual* herbicide to the soil where it will act through the root systems of weed seedlings and germinating seeds. Depending on the chemical used, its effect may last from weeks to several months. In practice, soil acting residual herbicides are the most common group used in vegetable production although translocated foliar sprays of compounds such as glyphosate play an important role in ridding land of perennial weeds prior to vegetable cultivation. The timing of herbicide application can be varied in several ways as illustrated diagramatically in Fig. 6.2. When the treatment is applied before the crop is sown then it is referred to as a *pre-sowing treatment*. If weeds had already emerged at this stage then either a contact or a translocated herbicide could be applied to their foliage as a control measure. Where the weed seeds had not

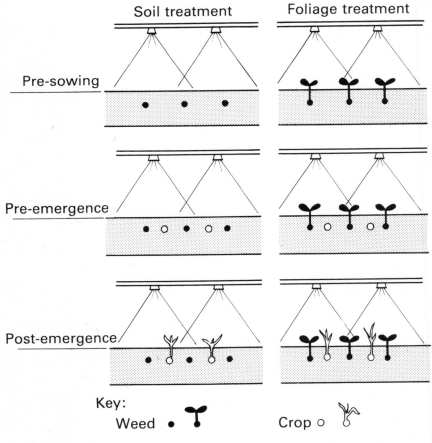

Fig. 6.2. Methods used for the spray application of herbicides.

germinated then a pre-sowing application of a residual herbicide onto the soil would be necessary to delay future weed problems.

Once the crop has been sown then spraying treatments are classified as either *pre-emergence* or *post-emergence*, where emergence refers to the actual crop and not the weed population. Again the choice of herbicide will depend on the stage of development of the weeds and may be residual, contact or translocated, although in the presence of the crop plant a measure of selectivity is also essential.

Selective toxicity

Reference has been made already to the complexity of selective toxicity in herbicides. Some understanding of the factors involved is essential for the safe use of the many compounds available to the vegetable grower.

When a chemical is applied to the foliage, the degree of its toxicity is partly dependent on the volume of spray retained. In some instances the weeds may retain more than the crop and this difference will contribute towards selectivity. Attributes such as leaf angle and arrangement, and the presence of surface waxes in and on the leaf cuticle differ considerably between species. For example the near vertical leaves of onions intercept far less spray than the more horizontal leaves of many weed species. Timing of spray application to onions is critical and herbicides should not be applied between emergence and the post crook stage (fig. 6.3). The leaves of peas have a particularly water repellent surface which causes large droplets to bounce or run off their surface. The use of the dinitrophenol herbicides as post emergence sprays on peas makes particular use of this attribute in achieving selectivity. Leaf age can have a significant effect on selectivity as young leaves generally have less wax on their surfaces than older ones. Environmental factors will also modify levels of susceptibility with, for example, cool dry weather resulting in more leaf wax production than warm humid conditions. It is possible to accentuate the effects of different levels of interception and retention by varying both the volume of spray applied and also its drop size. Wetting agents are also used as a means of increasing spray retention.

Although varying degrees of retention can contribute significantly to levels of selectivity, the main basis of selectivity depends on different biochemical responses between crop and weed species. Following uptake, the active chemical can disrupt a number of processes including respiration (DNP, dinoseb, PCP, ioxynil and

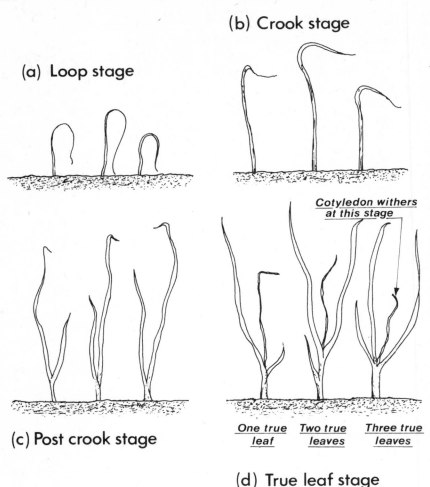

(a) Loop stage

(b) Crook stage

(c) Post crook stage

Cotyledon withers at this stage

One true leaf

Two true leaves

Three true leaves

(d) True leaf stage

Fig. 6.3. Stages of early growth of onions.

bromoxynil all operate in this way), photosynthesis (for example carbamates, triazines and uracils), and others such as protein and lipid synthesis. Many chemicals will operate via more than one process. Chemical selectivity can also operate at a number of levels. For example simazine is rapidly converted to a non-toxic compound following absorption by sweet corn (maize). Conversely other compounds such as MCPB are non-phytotoxic until converted to MCPA within susceptible species.

Soil applications
The main method of herbicide uptake following soil application is

by mass flow in soil water, thus rainfall and irrigation can have significant effects on weed control programmes. Some uptake will also occur by diffusion either as vapour or in solution but these pathways are generally less important. In deciding application rates it should be recognised that some adsorption onto soil particles and organic matter will take place, the amount depending on both the soil type and the chemical. Adsorption on sandy soils is minimal but can be quite significant in the case of clays and even more so in organic, peat soils. Some chemicals are influenced by soil types far more than others and in some instances it may be necessary to apply doses as much as one hundred times more concentrated on organic soils relative to sands. Table 6.1 gives examples of herbicides in relation to their degree of reaction to soil type.

Table 6.1   Influence of soil type on herbicides

Relatively unaffected by soil type	Strongly affected by soil type
Dalapon	Chlorpropham
EPTC	Linuron
2,3,6-TBA	Simazine
TCA	Terbacil

Following herbicide application to the soil it is often advantageous to incorporate the material into the surface layers by harrowing or rotavation. In this way the active chemicals are brought into the zone of germinating weeds, making the treatment less dependent on rainfall. Incorporation will also reduce losses by volatilization. By careful sowing it is possible to place crop seeds beneath the herbicide layer, thus achieving a level of selectivity as the crop roots will be growing into untreated soil. In practice the method can only be used with herbicides that are not taken up by underground portions of the stem and which are fairly immobile in the soil profile so they are not likely to be washed down to the developing crop roots.

Herbicide degradation
Some residual action is of course essential in herbicides applied to the soil but long term persistence will affect future cropping programmes. The safe period between application and the sowing or planting of successive crops will depend on many factors

including the herbicide, the prevailing weather conditions, the soil type and the crop. Degradation will occur in time as a consequence of both chemical and microbiological action and in both instances soil temperature will have a marked effect on the rate. Examples of relative herbicide persistence in soil are given in table 6.2.

Table 6.2   Relative herbicide persistance in soil

Short persistence (less than 3 months)	Medium persistence (3–6 months)	Long persistence (more than 6 months)
Aziprotryne	Chlorbromuron	Atrazine
Carbetamide	Cycloate	Lenacil
Chloropropham	Dinitramine	Methazole
Cyanazine	EPTC	Simazine
Dalapon	Linuron	Terbacil
Metoxuron	Tri-allate	TCA
Terbutryn	Trietazine	Trifluralin

Pests

In the present context the most important pests attacking vegetables are insects and nematodes, although it is recognised that other groups including birds and mammals are able to cause significant damage to growing crops. As in the case of weed infestation, damage caused by pests may not simply reduce yields but may also lower the quality of produce and in extreme cases render it unmarketable. Complete pest control is uneconomic if not impossible, although most vegetable crops are susceptible to attack at some stage in their growth and some level of protection is generally necessary.

Pest control

In many instances simple cultural techniques will reduce the chances of insect attack or at least reduce the level of incidence. Keeping land clear of weeds which may act as alternative host plants for overwintering pests is one way of reducing the chance of serious outbreaks. Remaining crop residues may also form loci for future attacks and should be removed or ploughed into the soil. Windbreaks may form a home for both harmful and beneficial insects although tree species which form alternative pest hosts to crop should clearly be avoided. Willows (*Salix spp.*) for example, play an important part in the life cycle of the willow-carrot aphid (*Cavariella aegopodii*) and should therefore not be used where carrots are grown. *Alnus spp.* are a more appropriate choice for windbreaks in such locations.

Crop rotations are less adhered to on today's specialist farms but they are still a useful method for reducing the build-up of pests, particularly soil-borne species. The use of crop rotation is one of the few practical methods of dealing with eelworms, as techniques of partial soil sterilisation are particularly expensive for use in relation to the field production of vegetables. Where the pea cyst nematode (*Heterodera goettingiana*), which attacks broad beans as well as peas, is a problem, then host plants should be grown no more frequently than one year in four and preferably less frequently. A long rotation used in conjunction with a systemic nematicide such as oxamyl will prevent serious damage from most nematodes.

Plant breeders are making an important contribution to plant protection by producing pest resistant cultivars. Immunity to pest attack is rare but the lettuce cultivars Avoncrisp and Avondefiance, bred at the National Vegetable Research Station, Britain, are for all practical purposes in this category being highly resistant to attack by lettuce root aphid (*Pemphigus bursarius*). Any degree of resistance, however, is potentially useful as it is likely to combine with cultural and chemical control methods to increase their efficiency.

Irrespective of whether a plant is genetically resistant to pest attack, it will usually suffer less if it is healthy. Cultural factors such as nutrition, irrigation, correct spacing, etc., will all help to produce plants that are less likely to succumb to damage.

Considerable efforts are made by growers to ensure earliness and continuity of production but this will often mean that crops are exposed to peak periods of attack by certain pests. Where possible such periods of vulnerability should be avoided by adjusting sowing and planting dates. Very early and late sowings and plantings of brassicas will avoid the worst attacks of flea beetle (*Phyllotreta undulata*).

Under natural conditions pest populations are kept in balance by their predators and parasites. The biological control of pests of glasshouse crops has reached a high level of sophistication and is now common practice for many commercial crops. Research is being conducted on similar techniques for use on field crops but at present considerably more development is required, and for the majority of vegetable pests, it is necessary to resort to chemical techniques.

Chemical control techniques

The term pesticide is used collectively to describe all chemicals used in the control of pests. The majority of these chemicals are in fact used specifically to control insect pests and the term insecticide is then appropriate although acaricides and nematicides, for example, are used in the control of other groups.

For a chemical to be an effective pesticide it must meet a number of requirements including high toxicity to the pest but low toxicity to the plant and other life forms. In addition it must be easy to apply and economical to use. In practice it is extremely difficult to achieve this combination of attributes and most pesticides are potentially dangerous to man and wildlife if used incorrectly.

Mode of action

Although there is some overlapping in the mode of action of different chemicals there are five main types which have an important bearing on their use for controlling different types of pest.

- Stomach poisons operate through the pest ingesting plant material that has been sprayed with the chemical.
- Contact poisons pass through the pest's integument and must therefore be brought into direct contact with the pest.
- Fumigants. The fumigant action of some pesticides depends on the chemical vapours entering into the respiratory system via the spiracles.
- Ovicides are able to kill specifically the eggs of pests.
- Systemic poisons are able to move within the plant's translocation system and are ingested by sap feeding insects.

Many groups of chemicals include members which are effective as insecticides. The principal groupings are organochlorines, organophosphates and carbamates.

The organochlorine chemicals include a number of very effective insecticides but they suffer from the disadvantage of being very persistent and are therefore not widely used in vegetable production. DDT was the first member of this group to be used extensively, but it is now subject to legislation limiting its use. Gamma-HCH and aldrin, too, have restricted use in, for example, wire worm control of potatoes.

Organophosphates represent a very wide range of useful pesticides, many of which are systemic in action. Again there is a potential problem of persistence and precautions are necessary to reduce side effects on wildlife.

The carbamate group of pesticides has the important characteristic of low mammalian toxicity and is therefore particularly useful for application to vegetable crops.

Many other groups of chemicals are effective as pesticides, including a number of plant derivatives such as nicotine and pyrethrin and the closely related synthetic pyrethroids. These, and groups such as the formamidines, are useful alternatives when insect pests develop resistance to particular compounds. Development of resistance can occur with any chemical but has been most common within the organophosphates.

Table 6.3 gives examples of the principal groups of pesticides together with indications of their use.

Diseases

As in the case of damage by insect and other pests, the development of diseases in a growing crop may result in both lower yields and reduced quality. Viruses, bacteria and fungi can all cause serious crop losses although the latter group are more diverse and represent the most serious threat to vegetable production.

The viruses which affect vegetables are generally either transmitted via the seed, (or vegetative propagules such as potato tubers) or by mobile vectors including nematodes and sap sucking insects, particularly aphids. In such instances the spread of virus may be prevented or reduced by the appropriate control of pest and weed species which act as alternative hosts to the vectors. No effective chemical is available for the control of viruses under field conditions and the only sure way of avoiding the problem is to start with virus-free seed and plants followed by rigorous vector control.

Bacterial diseases are more frequently associated with rotting during storage but they can also present a problem in some growing crops, particularly under very wet conditions. Bacterial diseases may be soil-borne and can enter roots and tubers through lenticels and wounds. Both rain and irrigation can also spread bacterial disease from plant to plant. Control is difficult and the best way to avoid bacterial problems is to start with clean, healthy planting material.

The fungal diseases of economic significance generally have the

Table 6.3 Examples of pesticides used in vegetable production classified in their chemical groupings

Pesticide	Comments and examples of use
Organochlorines	
*Aldrin	Persistent; used as dust for wireworm control in potatoes
*DDT	Persistent; chafer grub in potato and cutworm in carrots
*Endosulfan	Control of pests on brassicas grown for seed production
Gamma-HCH	Used in mixtures with other compounds as seed treatment
Organophosphates	
Chlorfenvinphos	Granules and liquid; cabbage root fly and early generation carrot root fly
Demeton-S-methyl	Systemic; aphid control in range of crops
Diazinon	Wettable powder; cabbage root fly and late generation carrot root fly
Formothion	Systemic; aphid control on range of crops
Iodofenphos	Cabbage root fly control in Brussels sprout buttons
Phorate	Systemic; aphids, early generation carrot root fly and frit fly in maize
Pirimiphos-methyl	Aphids, caterpillars on brassicas and frit fly in maize
Carbamates	
Aldicarb	Systemic insecticide and nematicide; potato cyst nematode and aphids
Carbofuran	Systemic; granules used in control of cabbage root fly, aphids, flea beetle, etc.
Ethiofencarb	Systemic; aphid control on potatoes
Pirimicarb	Aphid control on legumes and potatoes

* The use of these chemicals is restricted under the Pesticides Safety Precautions Scheme.

characteristic of rapid rates of multiplication given the appropriate environmental conditions, and efficient methods of dissemination. Once again the importance of starting with clean propagation material must be stressed and in particular seed treatments may be necessary to prevent the transmission of seed-borne diseases such as white rot in onions (*Sclerotium cepivorum*) and celery leaf spot (*Septoria apiicola*) in celery.

The majority of plant infecting fungi produce spores at some stage in their life cycle and these are generally distributed over large distances by air movements. Water also plays an important role in the transmission of spores and their subsequent germination on a host plant with the consequence that rain and irrigation may play a part in the build-up of disease problems. Movement of soil water will also help distribute the mobile spores of the important soil-borne disease of brassicas, club root (*Plasmodiophora brassicae*).

Disease control

The approaches to disease control are in many ways similar to pest control. Prevention is usually easier than cure and although routine spraying of fungicides may sometimes be necessary there are cultural methods which also play an important role in minimising the dangers of crop losses. Resistant cultivars have been produced for a number of vegetable crops although the efforts of plant breeders are often thwarted by the ability of the fungi to produce new forms or physiological races which are less affected by this form of resistance.

Crop rotations have been referred to in relation to weed and pest problems and they play a similar role in reducing the incidence of fungal disease. Club root in particular requires a long period without access to brassicas (crop or weed species) which in practice necessitates a rotation of at least seven years. This pathogen also thrives best in acid soils so liming may also be necessary to reduce its incidence.

Other cultural techniques hinge on hygiene and healthy plant production. Crop residues should be destroyed and vigorous plant growth should be achieved by correct spacing, nutrition, etc., Excessively high levels of nitrogen should be avoided as these may lead to excessive soft lush growth which may rapidly succumb to disease attack.

Chemical control techniques
Chemicals play an essential role in the control of plant diseases in intensive systems of vegetable production. They can be used both to protect crops from attack and to control diseases that are already present. They are, however, costly and potentially dangerous and must therefore be selected carefully and applied correctly.

As with pesticides, the use of soil sterilants is particularly expensive for general field use and it is more economic to apply smaller quantities of fungicides to seeds and young transplants to protect them from attack by soil-borne pathogens.

Crop sprays can be applied as protectants in which case leaves are coated with a deposit of a chemical which prevents the development of any fungus in contact with it. Repeated sprayings may be necesary to treat new growth and replace deposits on older leaves which may have been washed off by rain although 'stickers' may be incorporated in the spray to improve its retention on the plant surface.

Fungicides designed to control fungal infection of the crop must come into contact with the pathogen and coverage may be particularly critical. The existence of systemic fungicides which are distributed through the plant in its translocation system means that the timing and efficiency of application are less critical.

Many chemicals show fungicidal action. Prior to the development of organic compounds, inorganic materials based on sulphur and copper were widely used. The organic molecules now available are generally more efficient and selective in their mode of action. The development of systemic fungicides, such as benomyl and carbendzamin, has been an important contribution to disease control.

Methods of application

Pesticides and fungicides can be applied in a number of different formulations including dusts, granules, solutions, emulsions, aerosols and fumigants. The most commonly used formulations in commercial vegetable production are granules and water-based sprays.

The earliest form of attack that a crop may experience is often the result of seed- and soil-borne pests and diseases. Although chemical sterilisation of soil is common practice for high value glasshouse crops it is usually uneconomic for application to vegetable production under field conditions except in limited areas in, for example, seedbeds in which transplants are to be raised, when chemicals such as dichloropropene can be injected into the soil prior to sowing to kill nematodes, eggs and insects.

One of the most economic ways of applying chemicals for crop protection is to do so as a seed dressing. Seeds may be mixed with small quantities of insecticidal dust so that active particles adhering to the seed at planting are taken up by the seedling on germination, thus providing a level of protection. Gamma-HCH used as a seed dressing will protect brassicas from early attack by flea beetles, stem weevil and cabbage root fly and carrots can be protected in a similar way from damage by carrot root fly. Other chemicals used in this way include pirimiphos-ethyl which is recommended as a seed treatment for French and runner beans to protect them from bean seed fly damage. In a similar way seed dressings of fungicides such as benomyl will confer protection against a number of fungal diseases.

Seed treatment is in a sense an insurance against early crop damage, but the use of seed treatment to control *Botrytis allii* in onion reduces losses through neck rot in store following harvest. Seed treatment is a cheap way of ensuring that crops get off to a clean start and may save the expense of early post-emergence spray applications.

The increasing use of peat block and modular raised transplants has stimulated more investigations into the effects of incorporating protective chemicals into the growing media both before sowing and as a drench prior to planting out. In a similar way pesticides can be incorporated into gels used in the fluid drilling technique of establishing vegetables (Thompson *et al.*, 1982).

Further protection from soil-borne pests can be achieved by incorporating insecticidal granules in the soil, a procedure which is most economical when the treated area is confined to the immediate vicinity of the plant. This is most conveniently done at sowing along with the seed and fertiliser.

Although chemicals used as seed dressings and for soil application are selected to show some degree of persistence, they are generally not able to protect crops throughout their entire life. At some stage application of chemicals to the crop leaves may become necessary and the problems of chemical placement are thus more difficult. It is in such situations that the bed system of growing vegetables has the advantage that spray machinery can pass over the crop causing little damage. Dusting is a technique which has the advantage that large quantities of water do not have to be carried, thus saving time and energy, but it suffers from the danger of drifting. For this reason, water-based sprays are more appropriate for the application of chemicals to vegetable crops where the objective is usually to achieve maximum coverage with minimum drift.

Integrated approaches to pest and disease control

In this chapter we have considered some of the cultural and

chemical methods of pest and disease control. It is already apparent that no single technique is adequate by itself and that economic levels of control are best achieved by an integrated approach utilising a combination of different methods. Strict legislation and a greater awareness of environmental hazards have been partly responsible for a reduction in the number of new chemicals being made available for pest and disease control, a trend which is more likely to affect the specialist vegetable grower than the large scale arable farmer. From the point of view of the chemical company, the latter, with his extensive areas of a limited range of crops, represents a potentially larger customer. Vegetable producers are dealing with a much wider range of crop species and are concerned with a broader spectrum of pests and diseases.

Reference has already been made to the value of various control measures including the use of resistant cultivars, crop rotations and chemicals. The basis of any integrated programme must always be a thorough knowledge of the biology of the organisms that need controlling. It is insufficient to simply identify the problem (which in itself is not always easy), but it is also necessary to know, for example, the life cycle of a pest and what its alternative host plants are likely to be.

Pest and disease control start with the use of clean, healthy planting material and in this respect legislation plays an important part in an integrated programme of control.

Seed certification schemes, plant quarantine, import restrictions are all techniques of ensuring that certain diseases are not distributed via planting material. The build-up of certain injurious weeds is also reduced by legislation concerned with their compulsory destruction. It is likely that this form of legislative control will play an increasing role in the future.

Genetic resistance too has a very important part to play and although pest and disease resistant cultivars have been available for some time attention is now being directed increasingly towards partial resistance where total resistance is unavailable. The effect of even partial resistance, when combined with other control measures, has been shown to reduce the average crop losses and greater attention is being attached to this form of control in integrated programmes.

Many insect pests are able to communicate with each other over long distances by emitting extremely small quantities of volatile molecules known as pheromones. In many instances chemists have been able to synthesise identical compounds which can be used to assist in combatting pest problems. The male pea moth (*Laspeyresia nigricana*), for example, can be attracted and trapped to give information on population levels as a preliminary to crop spraying. The method can be adapted to reduce population numbers to confuse mating responses. Such techniques are increasingly likely to be used particularly in conjunction with other forecasting techniques.

The pattern of movement and population growth of pests and diseases can be monitored by sampling techniques and related to environmental conditions. The technique of forecasting outbreaks of potato blight from temperature and rainfall data was developed many years ago (Bourke, 1955). With the advent of the computer and improved techniques of communication it is becoming increasingly possible to forecast the outbreaks of pests and disease problems thus making timely control measures possible.

Biological control is an attractive alternative to the use of chemicals and could form a useful component of an integrated programme. However, apart from the use of *Bacillus thuringiensis* in the control of caterpillars there are as yet few instances where such methods have widespread application in the field scale production of vegetable crops. However, there are a number of active research investigations currently being conducted in this area. For example, investigations into the parasitism of onion white rot by nematodes of the genus *Trichoderma* offer promise as an alternative approach to controlling this particular problem (Entwistle and Marian, 1982).

Safety aspects of chemical use

By their very nature, chemicals used in the control of pests, diseases and weeds are potentially hazardous and their application can have adverse effects on humans and the environment far beyond their intended targets. The public are becoming more conscious of their environment and legislation is likely increasingly to impose constraints on the use of chemicals. Mandatory tolerance levels for chemical residues in edible crops are also likely to bring tighter controls on application. However, chemicals form an essential component of efficient vegetable production and potential dangers associated with their use can be minimised by a combination of legislation and recommended practices.

Details on approaches to safety will differ between countries but, for example, in the U.K. there is a Pesticides Safety Precautions

Scheme (P.S.P.S.) which is responsible for coordinating the various aspects of safety. This scheme ensures that no pesticide product is marketed until conditions have been defined to minimise the dangers of its use to growers applying the material, to consumers of treated foodstuffs, and to wildlife. A number of government Acts also seek to ensure safety in the use of chemicals and in their disposal. A grower should acquaint himself with all aspects of safety.

Many new chemicals are released on to the market and the Agricultural Chemicals Approval Scheme (A.C.A.S.) publishes an annual list (Ministry of Agriculture, Fisheries and Food, 1984) of approved chemicals with notes on their use including information on any restrictions that may apply.

References and further reading

Bourke, P.M.A. (1955) 'The forecasting from weather data of potato blight and other plant diseases and pests'. *Technical Note No. 10. World Meteorological Organisation*, **42**, 3–48.

Dixon, G.R. (1981) *Vegetable Crop Diseases*. London: MacMillan.

Entwistle, A.R. and Marian, S.E. (1982) 'Biological control of onion white rot'. *Annual report of National Vegetable Research Station for 1981*, p. 68.

Hewson, R.T. and Roberts, H.A. (1971) 'The effect of weed removal at different times on the yield of bulb onions'. *Journal of horticultural Science*, **46**, 471–483.

Hill, T.A. (1977) *The Biology of Weeds*. London: Edward Arnold.

Klingman, G.C., Ashton, F.M. and Noordhoff, L.J. (1975) *Weed Science: Principles and Practices*. New York: Wiley.

Martin, H. and Woodcock, D. (1983) *The Scientific Principles of Crop Protection*. 7th edn. London: Edward Arnold.

Ministry of Agriculture, Fisheries and Food (1984) *List of Approved Products and their uses for Farmers and Growers* (revised annually). London: H.M.S.O.

Roberts, H.A. (1976) 'Weed competition in vegetable crops'. *Annals of applied Biology*, **83** 321–324.

Roberts, H.A. ed. (1982) *Weed Control Handbook: Principles* 7th edn. Oxford: Blackwell Scientific Publications.

Scopes, N. and Ledieu, M. eds. (1980) *Pest and Disease Control in Vegetables, Potatoes and Sugarbeet*. London: British Crop Protection Council.

Thompson, A.R., Suett, D.L. and Percivall, A.L. (1982) 'The protection of carrots against carrot fly (*Psila rosae*) with granular and emulsifiable concentrate formulations of chlorfenvinphos incorporated in gels used for drilling pre-germinated seed in sandy-loam'. *Annals of Applied Biology*, **101**, 229–237.

Ware, G.W. (1983) *Pesticides: Theory and Application*. San Francisco: Freeman.

7 Irrigation

Introduction

Water is essential for plant growth and is a major determinant of crop productivity. Vegetable production in the more arid regions of the world would be impossible without some form of irrigation and in the wetter regions it is used on a large scale to overcome the problems caused by variability and unpredictability of rainfall. In addition to the more obvious benefits of irrigation on yield during periods of prolonged drought, it can also be used, for example, to improve the germination of seeds, to assist in the distribution of fertilisers and to facilitate the harvesting of root crops from dry soils. There can be few vegetable growing enterprises which could not benefit from the use of irrigation in some form although the availability of water and capital will often restrict its use.

Water availability to plants is determined by the balance between water evaporated from their leaves (transpiration) and the uptake of water from the soil through their roots. If the rate of transpiration exceeds the rate of uptake then deficits will develop within the plant tissues. This in turn will cause partial and eventually, complete closure of stomata, a response which will reduce the rate of water loss. Photosynthesis, however, is dependent on the entry of CO_2 through the stomatal openings into the leaf and conservation of water as a result of increasing stomatal resistance will therefore be at the cost of reduced growth. The development of water deficits within the plant is thus not a simple response to lack of rain but is brought about by a complex interaction between atmosphere, plant and soil factors. These are now considered in more detail.

Evaporative demand

The loss of water from a well watered plant is primarily a function of the weather. Differences between species are small compared with those resulting from the evaporative demand of the atmosphere.

Solar radiation, temperature, humidity and wind speed are the main determinants of transpiration and information on these parameters can be used as a basis for calculating irrigation requirements. Potential transpiration is defined as the amount of water lost from a healthy green crop fully covering the soil surface and adequately supplied with water. During the early stages of growth and in the case of widely spaced row crops the soil surface is incompletely covered by the leaf canopy. Water loss from a wet soil surface is, in practice, very similar to that from plant leaves but once the surface of the soil dries out the water loss from the soil is reduced markedly. It is possible to calculate the potential evaporation from standard meteorological data and, after allowing for incomplete soil cover, thus to estimate the plants' requirement for water.

A number of theoretical formulae have been derived for use in the calculation of potential evaporation, the most widely used being that of Penman (1948). More empirical approaches to estimating irrigation requirements are referred to later in the chapter.

The soil moisture reservoir

The amount of water that can be retained by a soil is determined by its pore space distribution and its organic matter content. The pores are formed between the irregular shaped mineral particles, the size distribution of which combine to give the soil its characteristic texture. When rain or irrigation water completely fills the pore space the soil is said to be *saturated* (fig. 7.1). Under such conditions plant root systems are deprived of oxygen, a situation which will eventually lead to root death. Following the application of water to

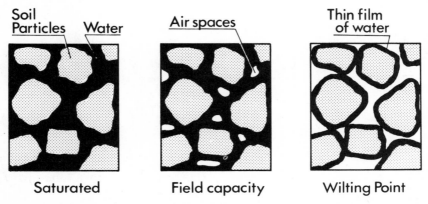

Fig. 7.1. Diagram showing soil moisture at different stages in the drying cycle.

the soil surface, gravity causes water to drain from the larger pores and is replaced by air. Drainage will continue until the pull of gravity equals the force at which the remaining water is retained by surface tension within the finer pores of the soil matrix. At this stage the soil moisture content is said to be at *field capacity* (FC). The time taken to reach this stage following rain or irrigation will depend on the soil type, although for many soils used in vegetable production drainage is usually negligible following a period of about two days. Soil samples taken at this stage can be used as a basis for determining field capacity or alternatively a laboratory test in which saturated samples are subjected to a low tension (often 0.05 bar) may be used. For practical purposes, field capacity represents the upper limit of water availability to plants. Water in excess of this value is transient, and if poor drainage results in higher levels being maintained for prolonged periods, then plants will suffer from water logging.

The volume of water held in a soil at field capacity will depend largely on its texture. Sandy soils, for example, consist of relatively large soil particles which pack together to form larger pore spaces which drain rapidly. In a similar way the finer textured clay soils contain much finer pore spaces which retain larger amounts of water. A sandy soil at field capacity may contain as little as 10% by volume of water compared with a value of as much as 60% for a clay.

In the absence of further rain or irrigation a plant will continue to extract water from the soil, initially at a rate corresponding to potential evaporation and then more slowly until it eventually wilts. If the wilting is irreversible and the plant will not recover in a humid atmosphere then the soil is said to be at its *permanent wilting point* (PWP) which thus represents the lower point of water availability to the plant. This stage of permanent wilting should not be confused with the temporary wilting that frequently occurs at midday under conditions of intense evaporation even when a soil is at, or near, field capacity.

Although there are some species differences it is common for most plants to suffer permanent wilting when the water in the soil is held in the remaining pore space at a tension of 15 bar and for practical purposes this fact may be used as a basis for a physical determination of this lower limit of water availability. On a volume basis, permanent wilting points in coarse sandy soils may lie between 0 and 10% whereas clays are more likely to contain between 30 and 40%.

The soil available water content (AWC) for plant growth is thus held in the soil between the limits of field capacity and permanent wilting point, although the water in this range is not necessarily all equally available. As permanent wilting is approached it becomes increasingly more difficult for the plant to extract water, stomatal closure becomes more prolonged and growth is reduced. Ideally irrigation should be carried out before this stage is reached.

The amount of water and the tension at which it is held in a soil are thus largely determined by the soil texture and consequent pore size distribution. Small but sometimes significant improvements to a soil's water holding capacity can be achieved by the addition of organic matter and other additives.

Examples of soil moisture retention curves (also called soil water characteristic curves) for contrasting soil types are shown in fig. 7.2, which also indicates their corresponding water contents. It should

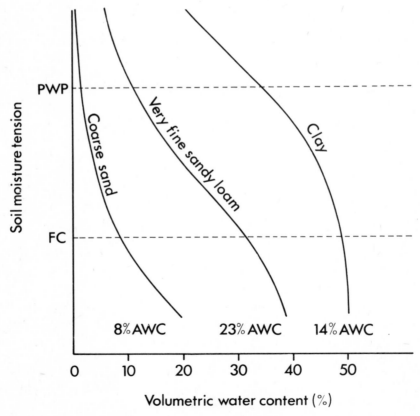

Fig. 7.2. Soil moisture retention curves for contrasting soil types.

be noted that high water contents at field capacity, which occur in the clay soils, do not confer the highest available water content, for a proportion of fine sand and silt are also desirable for maximum water availability. Table 7.1 gives further examples of soil types in terms of their available water contents. Once the moisture content falls below field capacity, movement of soil water virtually ceases. Water cannot, therefore, move towards plant roots and thus the only water available to the plant must be within its rooting range.

Table 7.1   Available water content of various soil types

Available water content (percentage by volume)		
Low (less than 12.5%)	Medium (12.5–20%)	High (more than 20%)
Coarse sand	Loamy sand	Very fine sandy loam
Loamy coarse sand	Clay	Silty loam
Coarse sandy loam	Sandy clay	Peaty soil
	Silty clay	
	Clay loam	
	Silty clay loam	
	Loam	

Plant factors influencing water availability

It should be apparent from the foregoing sections that the degree of canopy cover and the depth and spread of rooting have considerable influence on a plant's water supply. Increasing the plant spacing to reduce water loss is a realistic option if maximum yield is not the prime objective, although this approach will only prove beneficial if weeds are not allowed to colonise the bare soil. Cultural operations such as deep cultivation and fertiliser application leading to improved root growth will have a particularly beneficial effect on increasing the availability of water to a crop.

Calculation of irrigation requirements

A knowledge of potential transpiration rates will enable the grower to estimate the total amount of water required by a crop. Depending on the amount and its distribution this may, in part, be supplied by rainfall although it must be appreciated that there is a limit to the amount that can be stored in the soil reservoir and excess draining beyond the reach of plant roots is effectively lost. Similarly, depending on the slope, nature of the soil surface and rainfall intensity, a significant quantity of water can be lost through surface run off. In planning an irrigation scheme the grower will usually have access to statistics on past rainfall and average evaporation rates from which average future water requirements can be estimated. Some idea of the number of years in which irrigation is likely to prove profitable may also be derived from past weather statistics (see fig. 7.3).

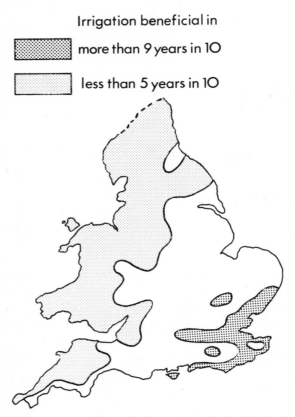

Fig. 7.3. Potential benefits from irrigation in England.

In the day-to-day management of any irrigation scheme the grower will have to answer two main questions: 'how much water should he apply?' and 'when should he apply it?'

It should be clear already that the answer to the first question will be affected largely by the weather in particular, the evaporation rate and the amount of rainfall. There are a number of alternatives available for providing information on evaporation rates from, at one extreme, running a full scale meteorological station from which Penman estimates of potential evaporation may be calculated, through to assuming the average rate for the time of year as estimated from past experience. In practice, the local agricultural advisory office can usually provide the required information on a timely basis or alternatively the average can be assumed as a working basis which can then be adjusted following receipt of more precise information. More empirical methods, such as the use of evaporation tanks, can also be used.

The measurement of rainfall presents more of a problem in that, although data is usually available through the meteorological service, there can be substantial spatial variations over very short distances. If a grower wishes to calculate his irrigation requirements with any degree of accuracy he should install one or more gauges on his own farm.

'When to irrigate?' is a more difficult question to answer. Leaving aside for the moment the important topic of management and cost, plants will grow best with their roots in soil at or near field capacity. To irrigate when the soil is at field capacity will result in not only loss of water but also of nutrients through leaching. To postpone irrigation until the soil is near or at wilting point will cause reduction in growth and eventually death of plants. The deficit that may be permitted to develop with little, if any, adverse effect on yield will be determined in part of course by the size of the soil moisture reservoir as described earlier but it is also species- and even cultivar-dependent. The matter is further complicated by the existence of moisture critical stages in the development of many species, a topic to be dealt with later. Having decided on a permissable or acceptable deficit, it is possible for a grower to operate a soil moisture budget taking into account both water losses by evaporation and gains from rainfall and irrigation. Irrigation application can then be timed to coincide with achievement of the permitted deficit which can then be replaced completely to restore the soil to field capacity. Partial replacement will leave a portion of the soil profile dry and this can be done deliberately if rainfall is expected to fall in the near future.

The application of this method of scheduling irrigation is illustrated graphically in fig. 7.4. The dashed lines represent the increasing deficit that would develop during each month as a consequence of evaporation in the absence of either rain or

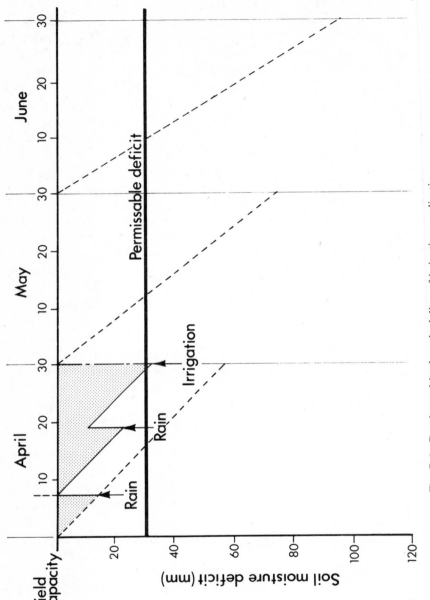

Fig. 7.4. Graph used in the scheduling of irrigation applications.

irrigation. The slopes of these lines are based on average monthly potential evaporation data for the area in question. In the example shown the soil is assumed to be at field capacity at the beginning of April. A deficit then starts to develop until field capacity is restored by either rain or irrigation. Sometimes the amount of rain will exceed the deficit, in which case the surplus will be lost as drainage. At other times rainfall may be less than the original deficit with the result that a new, lower deficit will be achieved. In this way the deficit will go through cycles of increasing and decreasing values until it reaches the 'permissable deficit'. At this stage, which can to some extent be anticipated on the basis of prevailing weather conditions, irrigation should be carried out to restore conditions to field capacity.

In practice, depending on water availability and its cost in relation to the value and response to irrigation of the crops grown, various strategies may be adopted although a clear understanding of the principles of water availability is essential for optimisation of the method. The budget approach is probably the most straightforward scientific approach to the problem of scheduling irrigation. Other techniques involving the measurement of soil moisture are prone to problems of sampling and in some instances instrumentation. The simplest approach of taking auger samples of soil from the rooting range of the crop and assessing its moisture content by feel is a useful adjunct to the budget method and serves as a check not only on the validity of the calculation but also on the efficacy of the method of water application.

Soil moisture tensiometers can also be installed in the crop although their use is restricted to conditions where soil moisture tension does not exceed 0.8 bar between irrigation applications, although this will not be a serious constraint for many soil types. Soil moisture resistance blocks will function over a wider range of soil moistures and when calibrated can provide useful information on the development of deficits beneath crops. They are, however, subject to calibration drift and can also be affected by the presence of varying fertiliser levels in the soil.

It can be argued that the plant itself is the best indicator of its own water requirement and plants do indeed show changes in leaf posture and colour in response to increasing moisture deficit. Stomatal movements are also a useful guide to increasing water shortage but in general the problems of sampling and the need for special equipment have precluded the use of plants for irrigation scheduling in anything but the most extreme cases.

Moisture sensitive stage

Although moisture stress at any stage is likely to affect the overall growth of a plant, in some instances the economic part of many crops may not be affected to the same extent unless the stress occurs at a particular stage in development. For example, peas will produce maximum yields in spite of drought prior to flowering providing the plant does not suffer from water shortage during the period of fertilisation and pod swelling. This type of moisture sensitivity is common to many species where the reproductive part of the plant forms the economic yield and the grower should ensure that stress does not occur during these periods. When the amount of water available for irrigation is limited it is important to use it on vegetables currently in a moisture sensitive stage of growth.

In leafy vegetables such as brassicas, yields can be adversely affected by soil moisture deficits at any time in their development although the stages when such crops are most likely to suffer from stress is during establishment and in the period prior to harvest.

Sources of water for irrigation

An adequate and dependable supply of water is essential for any irrigation programme. It must of course be free from toxic minerals and salts and be biologically clean, a factor of particular importance with salad crops which are consumed raw. Brackish water containing more than 500mg/litre of salt should not be used for irrigation. The main categories of supply are surface sources, such as rivers, streams and lakes, ground water sources from boreholes and from the public main water supply system. It most instances a licence will be required for extraction of water from any of these sources and this will usually specify the quantities that may be extracted during specified periods. Depending on the source of supply and imposed constraints on its use there may be a need to provide farm storage facilities to carry the irrigation programme through periods of peak demand. The quantities of water required for irrigation can be extremely large. For example, it requires more than 100 000 litres to cover one hectare with one centimetre of water and even in temperate regions this may be needed more than twice a week during periods of drought. The engineering and economic aspects of providing water to the farm are beyond the scope of the present text.

Methods of application

The choice of method for applying irrigation water will depend on a number of important factors. One of the more important of these is the *infiltration capacity* of the soil, which is a measure of the maximum rate that water can infiltrate it at a given time. As the soil becomes wetter the rate will decline until an equilibrium value is reached which depends principally on soil texture and structure characteristics. Typical values of equilibrium infiltration capacities for selected soils are shown in table 7.2.

Table 7.2. Equilibration infiltration capacities of selected soils

Equilibration infiltration capacity (mm/h)			
Very high (more than 100)	High (20–100)	Medium (5–20)	Low (less than 5)
Coarse sand	Sandy loam	Loam	Clay
Loamy coarse sand	Fine sandy loam	Silt loam	Silty clay
Loamy sand	Loamy fine sand	Clay loam	Sandy clay

Infiltration capacities represent the maximum rate at which soils will accept water, but for irrigation purposes allowance must also be made for soil variability and the effects of uneven application.

Other factors influencing the choice of method for applying water include crop type, field shape and topography and such considerations as power and labour availability. The main categories to choose from are:

- Surface irrigation where water is run over the surface so that it infiltrates into the soil.
- Sub-irrigation where water is introduced into the soil at depth until capillary action raises it into the root zone.
- Overhead irrigation which simulates the effect of rain.
- Trickle or drip irrigation.

Surface irrigation
Surface irrigation is one of the oldest techniques for applying water to plants and is still widely used for vegetable production in many parts of the world. In order to achieve a uniform supply of water to the root zone with a minimum amount of percolation, sufficient only

to leach out harmful salts, is a complex process depending on both hydraulic and soil factors. Soil characteristics such as infiltration capacity and drainage rate are difficult to modify but there is considerable scope for adjusting and controlling the hydraulic factors. Discharge rate, slope of the run and shape of the field furrows all influence the extent and rate at which the water enters the soil profile. Various systems have been developed. For example crops may be grown on raised beds separated by furrows through which water is introduced prior to its lateral infiltration into the root zone. At the other extreme, areas of level ground surrounded by low earth banks can be constructed to form basins which may be periodically flooded.

Sub-irrigation

The attractions of sub-irrigation techniques over other methods are that water losses from open water and wet soil surfaces can be eliminated and surface operations are not impeded by the presence of either pipes or ditches, etc. The use of sub-irrigation is largely confined to sites where the soil profile is characterised by high horizontal permeability and low vertical permeability. Such situations exist in, for example, the reclaimed polders of the Netherlands. Fields are surrounded by deep ditches and water levels are maintained constantly by either adding or removing water via pumps. In arid climates provision must be made for periodically leaching the root zone to wash out harmful concentrations of salts which build up as a consequence of continued upward movement of dissolved salts from the water table. In more humid climates there is more likely to be an annual excess of rainfall over evaporation which will minimise such problems.

A refinement of the method involves the use of perforated pipes buried at a depth of about 0.5 m with similar lateral spacing depending on the permeability of the soil. Such systems are expensive to install and maintain and are consequently not widely used.

Overhead irrigation

The three main types of overhead distribution equipment are spray lines, medium to low pressure rotary sprinklers and high pressure rotary rain guns although the latter are not widely used in vegetable production because of the physical damage they can cause to crops and soil. Each type of equipment can be mounted on self-propelled supports making some degree of automation possible.

The use of oscillating spray line irrigation is usually confined to high value crops such as salads. Output and spray patterns are in part determined by the size and distribution of nozzles along the length of the tube, although typical rates are in the order of 3 mm/hour.

Overhead rotary sprinklers are widely used for irrigating vegetables. There are many types available, designed to operate at different pressures. A typical line of medium pressure sprinklers uses heads that water a circle of about 33 m and depending on spacing, etc., will deliver approximately 6 mm/hour. Irrigation equipment is referred to again later in chapter 11, under machinery.

Trickle systems for use in the field production of vegetables have been developed from those used for glasshouse crops. Various types of drip nozzles and capillary tubes have been used to produce a trickle or series of drips from a main lateral laid between the crop rows. Such systems are generally more expensive than spray lines or sprinklers but the use of various types of layflat polythene tubing, either perforated or sown along its length to permit seepage, has reduced the cost although its use is most practical in small scale units. A major advantage of trickle systems is that they leave most of the surface dry, thus reducing water loss through direct evaporation.

A number of factors will need to be considered in the choice of suitable equipment for use in vegetable production. In recent years the trend has been towards lower application rates and automated movement of sprinklers, thus reducing soil and crop damage and keeping labour costs to a minimum.

References and further reading

Carr, M.K.V. (1981a) 'The role of irrigation in vegetable production'. In *Vegetable Productivity*, ed. C.R.W. Spedding, London: MacMillan, pp. 116–135.

Carr, M.K.V. (1981b) 'Timing and supply of water in relation to quality'. In *Quality in Stored and Processed Vegetables and Fruit*, eds. P.W. Goodenough and R.K. Atkin, London: Academic Press, pp. 117–128.

Hogg, W.H. (1967) *Atlas of Long Term Irrigation Need*. London: H.M.S.O.

Ministry of Agriculture, Fisheries and Food (1977) *Water for Irrigation*. Reference Book 202, London: H.M.S.O.

Ministry of Agriculture, Fisheries and Food (1982) 5th edn. *Irrigation*. Reference Book 138, London: H.M.S.O.

Penman, H.L. (1948) 'Natural evaporation from open water, bare soil, and grass'. *Proceedings of the Royal Society, Series A*, **193**, 120.

Salter, P.J. and Goode, J.E. (1967) *Crop Responses to Water at Different Stages of Growth*. East Malling: Commonwealth Agricultural Bureaux.

Vittum, M.T. and Flocker, W.J. (1967) 'Vegetable crops'. In *Irrigation of Agricultural Lands*, eds. R.M. Hagan, H.R. Haise and T.W. Edminster, American Society of Agronomy, pp. 674–685.

Withers, B. and Vipond, S. (1974) *Irrigation: Design and Practice*. London: Batsford.

8 Harvesting

Harvesting is the final cultural operation on a crop prior to marketing. The timing and method of harvesting are determined not only by the species of vegetable in question but also by the method of production and the proposed outlet. The consumer is becoming increasingly concerned with quality aspects which means that a grower must not only grow a good quality crop but it must be harvested and marketed in perfect condition if it is to achieve the high price premiums. Economic factors must clearly play an important part in deciding when and how a crop is harvested. In the case of vegetables such as potatoes and carrots which are grown for their storage organs, delays in harvesting may result in increased yields but at a lower unit prices. Similarly hand harvesting and trimming of, for example, Brussels sprouts may achieve high premiums for quality but at the expense of high labour cost.

There has been a revolution in harvesting techniques ranging from multiple selective hand harvesting, to once-over harvests aided in part by machine, through to the complete mechanical harvester. Cultivars have been selected to suit the harvesting system and the trend has been towards a greater uniformity in time of maturity making possible the once-over harvest. Genetic selection on its own is insufficient and growing systems have been modified to give more uniformity in growth and access for machinery, etc. Traditionally, produce has been transferred to a packhouse following harvest where the final trimming, grading and packing for market takes place. The development now, particularly for salad crops, is to carry out as much as possible of the operation in the field so that produce reaches the farm gate ready for market.

This chapter examines the various factors concerned with harvesting including pre- and post-harvest treatments. Further treatment of marketing and storage topics is provided in later chapters and examples of harvesting machinery are dealt with in chapter 11.

Date of harvesting

Many approaches are taken to ensure that the consumer may have access to a continuous supply of vegetables throughout the year. Invariably, seasonal constraints result in specific crops being unavailable for harvest during certain periods when supplies can only be obtained by importation from areas having a different climatic pattern, from storage or from processed sources.

When aiming for a specific harvest period one of the first factors to consider is the choice of cultivar. Many features confer earliness on a vegetable but the ability to survive and grow rapidly at low temperatures is an important characteristic. A large number of vegetable species are biennials and flowering or 'bolting' is triggered by low temperatures during the cold winter weather between the two growing seasons. In practice, young plants of such species will 'bolt' if sown too early when they may receive sufficient exposure to low temperatures to trigger the flowering response. Early cultivars have therefore been selected having reduced tendencies to bolt unless exposed to prolonged periods of low temperature. Plant size is also critical in relation to the bolting response and in the case of carrots, for example, it is most pronounced during the five to eight leaf stage. Overwintering of onions, based on Japanese cultivars, can be achieved by sowing at a date which will result in seedlings being large enough to survive the low winter temperature but too small to respond to the flower inducing effects of low temperatures.

Thus by choosing appropriate cultivars and sowing dates some control over harvest date may be achieved. Subsequent growth and development are determined largely by the prevailing weather conditions and precision in forecasting harvest dates is limited as much by difficulties in forecasting weather as by those of predicting crop responses to this weather.

Temperature is a major determinant of crop development and empirical formulae based on this parameter have been used successfully as a guide to harvest date. Ontario heat-units have been used as a guide to harvesting dates for a number of crops including maize and peas.

The stage of maturity of a vegetable crop has an important bearing on the date of harvesting. Although delays in harvesting are in many instances associated with increased yields they are often associated with losses in quality and flavour. In the case of peas, for example, increased maturity is associated with a conversion of sugars to starch and a corresponding change in texture. Immature peas are smaller, sweeter and more tender and the optimum stage of harvesting can be determined using an instrument known as a tenderometer which measures the shear strength of a sample of peas. In the case of carrots, size is particularly important for most market outlets and although this can be controlled to some extent by choice of variety and plant population, harvest date too can be an important determinant.

In some instances there may be separate markets for a particular species at different stages of maturity. Vegetable marrows, for example, may be either harvested at an advanced stage of development when they are called marrows or at a more immature stage when they are known as courgettes (or zucchini). The lower yields resulting from such earlier harvesting are usually compensated for by the higher price. The option of harvesting at different stages in theory implies a great flexibility for the grower although in practice he will normally plan his cropping programme to supply specific markets.

The harvesting of maize as sweet corn is designed to take advantage of the higher level of sugars prior to their conversion to starch in the mature grain. The optimum stage is usually indicated by the wilting and browning of the silk (styles) but in recent years there has been a small market for mini-cobs which are taken at a very early stage of development when, after cooking, they can be eaten in their entirety.

Leafy vegetables such as cabbages are usually allowed to heart up prior to harvest when they will be at their peak in yield and also provide a high proportion of tender, blanched internal leaves. The harvesting of spring greens which are picked at a much earlier stage helps provide a supply at a season when hearted cabbages are not readily available and determination of optimum harvesting date will then depend on prevailing prices and potential increases in yield from delaying the operation.

Pre-harvest treatments

All cultural operations are in effect pre-harvest treatments and will have some influence on the harvesting operation. However, there are a number of treatments that are specifically carried out to facilitate harvesting or to improve some aspect of the harvested crop. Bulb onions intended for storage are often sprayed with maleic hydrazide two weeks in advance of harvesting before leaves die back or are removed by the harvesting process. This compound is translocated to the onion bulb where it acts as a sprout suppressant, inhibiting the production of further leaves during storage.

Practical methods for delaying senescence in green crops would have considerable benefit in delaying harvesting dates. Pre-harvest sprays of cytokinins have been demonstrated to have potential application in this respect but have not yet reached the stage of commercial application. A more widespread application of growth regulators is the use of such compounds as diquat to effectively reduce foliage of root crops such as potatoes in order to facilitate harvesting. Deleafing is also an advantage prior to mechanical harvesting of Brussels sprouts, although chemical applications are not possible in this instance and leaves must either be broken off or cut with specially designed knives at harvesting.

A pre-harvest treatment that may be carried out on Brussels sprouts to accelerate the development of the upper buttons thus bringing forward the harvest date is the process of stopping. This process, which removes the growing point of the plant, has the effect of destroying apical dominance but if carried out too early it will cause the upper buds to 'blow' or to start developing as new shoots. Timing of the operation is fairly critical and should be carried out about four weeks in advance of summer harvesting and 10 weeks prior to winter harvesting.

Spraying in relation to harvest date

Chemical sprays used for crop protection may have beneficial effects beyond the harvest date since produce free from pest damage and diseases will usually have a longer shelf life. The use of chemicals as an aid to prolonging the storage life of vegetables will be discussed in the next chapter. Where sprays are applied, precautions should always be taken to ensure that unacceptable residues do not remain on edible crops at harvest where they could be toxic to the consumer or could cause tainting, rendering them unpalatable. These precautions are equally important whether the produce is being harvested for the fresh market or for processing.

The use of the more toxic pesticides, in particular the more persistent organochlorines such as DDT, is now severely restricted thus minimising the chances of them appearing at significant levels in crops. Chemicals recommended for use on vegetables approaching their harvest date are more short-lived and will breakdown before reaching the consumer providing instructions on their use are carefully adhered to. For example, the systemic organophosphorus insecticide demeton-S-methyl should not be applied to edible crops within three weeks of harvest whereas the carbamate insecticide pirimicarb can be applied to within three days of harvest.

Apart from any potential toxic effects a number of crop protection chemicals can produce taints and off-flavours in treated produce. Rigorous testing is carried out on such chemicals to determine the likelihood of this occurring and recommendations on their use includes information on possible tainting problems (Lyon, 1981). One compound, HCH, has caused serious tainting problems in potatoes and carrots grown on land that had been treated as long as ten years earlier although this is fortunately an exception. The effects of the insecticide malathion are short-lived and the minimum interval required between the last application and marketing of a vegetable crop is only one day. However, to avoid possible tainting a minimum of four days is recommended, which should be increased to seven in the case of vegetables intended for processing.

Hand harvesting

Increasing labour costs have led to a decline in hand harvesting of vegetables although many species do not lend themselves to machine harvesting in spite of considerable effort by plant breeders and agricultural engineers. The decline in production of runner beans, for example, has been brought about as a consequence of the need to hand pick this crop at frequent intervals if quality and yield are to be maintained.

One approach adopted by growers in favourable areas has been to operate 'pick your own' systems where consumers pay for the produce that they harvest themselves. This has advantages for both grower and consumer but presents additional problems in growing the crop and with high levels of wastage, yields are inevitably much lower.

Where there is a sufficiently high premium for quality, hand harvesting may in fact be preferable since humans are far better equipped to make accurate assessment of the suitability of a fresh vegetable for market and to carry out any necessary trimming operation. Once-over hand harvesting will enable the substandard produce to be rejected in the field. Selective multiple hand harvesting of, for example, cauliflower will ensure that in spite of variations in stages of development each will be harvested at its optimum condition.

Semi-automatic systems

Between the extremes of harvesting by hand or totally by machine, there exists a range of opportunities for automating various parts of the process and thus reducing the role of operators to those aspects which require the most skill. The use of semi-automatic harvesters is common for Brussels sprouts, whereby the stems are harvested mechanically before being fed manually to various designs of stripping head which remove the sprouts. Final grading can be carried out mechanically after passing along inspection conveyors where damaged and diseased sprouts can be removed by hand.

In a similar way crisphead lettuce harvesting can be largely mechanised with only the process of trimming prior to overwrapping being carried out by hand. The entire operation in this instance can be carried out in what are effectively mobile packing units built around a tractor.

Machine harvesting

It has been argued that any vegetable crop that cannot be harvested mechanically will disappear as a consequence of competition from those crops that can be successfully harvested in this way. Although such an extreme situation is unlikely to develop, there are likely to be consumer adjustments in eating habits. In some instances, for example, mechanisation has been successful in terms of supplying the processed market but not for the fresh product, a development which could lead to further increases in the consumption of processed foods or at least an increased price premium for the hand harvested vegetables.

Engineers are able to develop machines for harvesting any crop, the limitations being economic ones rather than technical problems. For simplicity in mechanisation, vegetables should preferably have the following characteristics. They should be uniform in size and time of maturity. The development of F_1 hybrids has gone a long way to ensuring this type of uniformity but attention to detail in terms of precision spacing and ensuring uniformity in seedling emergence will also contribute to reducing variability at harvest time.

Resistance to physical damage is also important and the development of harvesters for field-grown tomatoes in California has proceeded together with contributions from plant breeders in the form of cultivars with stronger skins which are more resistant to damage from the machines.

The mechanical harvesting of onions and root crops such as carrots presents few problems and the majority of larger growers will carry out the entire operation using appropriate machinery. The adoption of the so called 'direct harvesting' of onions by many growers in Britain has brought the entire operation under almost precision control and bulb qualities are no longer so dependent on the vagaries of the weather. In this method the foliage of the mature onions is topped in the field at approximately seven centimetres above the bulbs. After allowing the leaf trash and cut surfaces to dry for a few hours, the crop is mechanically undercut and lifted for immediate transfer to the store. Following the removal of surplus soil and leaf debris, bulb drying is carried out in a number of distinct stages. The first of these may take approximately three days and is a fairly rapid process carried out to remove surface moisture. The second stage, carried out more slowly and at higher humidities, is necessary to ensure the closing of the necks to seal the bulbs. This process will usually take around two weeks to complete. In the final stage temperatures and humidities are maintained at lower levels to prolong the storage life.

In no vegetable has mechanical harvesting developed to such an extent as that of the pea crop. The majority of the crop is now marketed frozen and production is usually centred on the processing factories to minimise delays between field and factory. The time taken should be no more than four hours and for optimum quality the date of harvesting is critical to within two days. The logistics of such an operation are complex and can only be carried out with specialised machinery and transport facilities. The original form of mechanisation involved a two stage process in which the pea vine, or haulm, including the pods was transferred to a stationary vining machine which then separated peas prior to further transport and processing. Modern harvesters run over the standing crop and remove the peas in a single operation.

Packing and grading

Following havesting, the crop must be packed and graded prior to marketing. Depending on the particular crop and its intended outlet, packing and grading may be carried out either in the field or at a specially designed and equipped packhouse. For the majority of vegetables, particularly salad crops, the entire process should be executed as quickly as possible to minimise losses through deterioration. This is particularly important during periods of hot weather.

Packing in the field can take a number of different forms and reference has already been made to the semi-automatic system of harvesting crisp lettuce in which trimming and overwrapping are conducted actually on the harvest machine itself. This form of mobile packing within a crop is adaptable to many species which require little additional treatment between harvesting and marketing such as brassicas and lettuce which do not require washing. There are a number of advantages in this approach. Firstly the delay between cutting and packing is reduced to a minimum. Quality control is also facilitated because trimmers and packers are able to immediately inform the people actually cutting the produce of any problems that may be occurring and harvesting standards can be adjusted accordingly. Any waste material can be left in the field thus contributing to soil nutrition and eliminating unnecessary transport costs. The major problems associated with mobile packing derive from the cost of investing in suitable machinery, although its physical size and weight can cause difficulties in operation and possible damage to soil structure. Such harvesting methods are usually used in conjunction with bed systems of production. A compromise between mobile packing and packing in a packhouse is to carry out the operation on the headland adjacent to the crop. This overcomes the problem of investment in specialised machinery but inevitably leads to increased delays and damage associated with the additional handling.

Transport of harvested produce to a central packhouse is usually essential for crops such as carrots and leeks which may need washing prior to marketing, but this approach has other advantages which make it attractive for a wide range of produce. The entire grading and packing can be made more efficient by the use of suitable machinery and it is also easier to maintain consistent standards as a result of the improved working conditions. In particular both staff and produce can be protected from adverse weather conditions.

Great care should be taken to prevent damage during transport to the packhouse particularly as this will involve bulk handling of produce. Careful handling should be carried out at all stages since bruises and cuts will lead to increased rates of respiration and invasion by spoilage organisms.

The final stages of grading and packing for market have taken on increasing importance in recent years and it is no longer sufficient to grow a crop – it must be marketed correctly. With increasing foreign trade, international standards are being defined. In the European Economic Community, for example, there are now a number of statutory grading standards for many vegetables and other crops defining classes for both size and quality characteristics.

Many supermarkets require produce to be pre-cooled before sale, a topic which is dealt with under storage in chapter 10.

Post-harvest losses

Post-harvest losses of vegetables are particularly serious in the tropics and may be of the order of 25% for root crops and higher for more perishable produce (Proctor *et al.*, 1981). Vegetables are very vulnerable to high rates of evaporation and to high temperatures which increase respiration rate and consequently cause losses in dry weight. In addition to these physiological losses they may also suffer loss from post-harvest spoilage brought about by pests and diseases whose incidence may in turn be aggravated by mechanical damage caused by harvesting and handling. Such losses can be reduced by many pre- and post-harvest practices.

Many of the cultural practices described in previous chapters can influence a crop's disposition to post-harvest losses. Choice of cultivar, nutritional aspects and pest and disease control, for example, will each have a bearing on the survival of a crop following harvest. One of the more far reaching effects of a pre-treatment on post-harvest losses is the fungicidal treatment of onion seed, which effectively prevents the development of neck rot of onions under storage perhaps months after harvest.

Botrytis cinerea is the most common fungus to be found on stored cabbage and its incidence can be reduced by pre- and post-harvest treatment with fungicides such as benomyl.

References and further reading

Burton, W.G. (1982) *Post-harvest Physiology of Food Crops*. London: Longman.
Cargill, B.F. and Rossmiller, G.E. *eds.* (1969) *Fruit and vegetable mechanization – Technological implications*. Michigan State University.
Kasmire, R.F. (1983) 'Influence of mechanical harvesting on the quality of nonfruit vegetables'. *Hortscience*, **18**, 421–423.
Lyon, D.H. (1981) 'Taints arising from use of crop chemicals. In *Quality in Stored and Processed Vegetables and Fruit*, eds. P.W. Goodenough and R.K. Atkin, London: Academic Press, pp. 267–272.

Ministry of Agriculture, Fisheries and Food (1982) *Bulb Onions*. Reference Book No. 348, London: Growers Books.

Proctor, F.J., Goodliffe, J.P. and Coursey, D.G. (1981) 'Post-harvest losses of vegetables and their control in the tropics'. In *Vegetable Productivity*, ed. C.R.W. Spedding, London: MacMillan, pp. 139–172.

Studer, H.E. (1983) 'Influence of mechanical harvesting on the quality of fruit vegetables'. *Hortscience*, **18**, 417–421.

9   Vegetable marketing

The transfer of vegetables from growers to consumers should be carefully planned if the transaction is to take place at a profit to the producer. Cropping should only proceed when the likely outlet has been recognised for there are many possibilities to consider, all of which will have a bearing as to when the crop is produced. Vegetables, along with many other horticultural products have characteristics which make marketing more difficult than products from other industries:

- Firstly they are perishable and although the shelf life of many root crops may extend over weeks, deterioration, particularly of the leafy salad crops, sets in soon after harvest.
- They are bulky in relation to their volume and this is aggravated by the further needs of packing to protect them from damage.
- There are often large distances between the areas of production and the main population areas where most of the marketing takes place.
- In spite of efforts to schedule production there will be considerable variation in supply as a result of variations in the weather. The supply of cauliflowers is, for example, particularly susceptible to fluctuations in weather.
- The final product is variable in terms of size and quality. Improved cultivars and growing techniques have done a great deal to remove many of the sources of variation and grading is an essential prerequisite for most markets.
- Although there has been an increase in farm size and the development of many large marketing co-operatives, overall production is largely in the hands of many uncoordinated producers.

There are numerous pathways via which the consumer can obtain vegetables from the grower. At one end of the scale the ultimate consumer can purchase direct from the producer via the farm shop or 'pick your own' system. This of course overcomes many of the problems of perishability and variability, and reduces some of the costs associated with other forms of marketing. It is not, however, suited to the large scale specialist grower although there are often opportunities for such growers to run a 'pick your own' unit as a subsidiary enterprise. The more common pathway is either through the wholesale markets or more directly through either the retailer or a processor. These main outlets are now considered in more detail.

Direct sales to the public

The increase in road side stalls and farm shops has paralleled increases in recreation and mobility. There are limits to the amount of produce that can be shifted in this way and the need to provide a wide range of produce as well as comply with local by-laws of, for example, parking and hygiene, reduce many of the attractions of using this direct route to the consumer. The 'pick your own' approach has the additional attraction of eliminating the costs of harvesting. This form of marketing originated for disposing of soft fruit crops such as strawberries and raspberries where problems of harvesting and perishability are even greater than those for fresh vegetables. However, to stay in business in the face of competition a grower must provide an increasing range of crops including vegetables. Indeed the trend has been increasingly towards recreation and the purchase of produce is becoming secondary to a day out in the country. To successfully run a 'pick your own' unit the grower must attend to many additional factors such as advertising, supervision, parking and toilet facilities. Choice of varieties and growing methods will have to be adjusted to suit this system of marketing. The public are looking primarily for freshness and flavour but the suitability of produce for freezing is also important. Almost all vegetables can and should be grown on a 'pick your own' unit but certain lines such as peas, beans and sweet corn are usually in high demand. Root crops which have to be dug are less popular. The emphasis on growing must be for quality and continuity. The normal recommendations for plant spacing must be modified to permit ready access. This form of marketing is associated with high levels of wastage which can be reduced by good planning and management although access to casual labour for harvesting excess production may be required when, for example, adverse weather has reduced customer demand.

Direct sales to retailers

There are a wide variety of retail shops marketing vegetables, ranging from the specialist greengrocer through to the large supermarket. The trend in sales to this market has been towards self service purchasing, together with a need for large and regular supplies of high quality pre-packed produce. The development of this demand has been largely responsible for recent trends in large scale specialist vegetable production and also the development and expansion of grower marketing co-operatives. The latter are particularly important with regard to crops such as runner beans which are still produced mainly by the smaller intensive growers. Suppliers have been forced to develop production programmes to give continuity of the right type and quality of product. Production seasons have to be lengthened by using new varieties and protected cropping. Pre-cooling and cold chain transport have also become important techniques for ensuring the customer receives produce in near perfect condition.

An important aspect of direct selling is the development of contractual agreements between the producer and retailer. Such agreements help to ensure a continuous supply for the retailer and assist growers in planning production schedules, although the success of such planning will still be affected by the weather and other environmental factors. Various forms of contract exist but it is common for a retailer to agree only on taking a particular quantity of produce at a particular time. Integration beween grower and contracting buyer may sometimes extend to the provision of technical advice and assistance, although this is more characteristic of the processing outlets to be discussed later.

It should be recognised that retail shops are not the only form of direct sales. Catering consumption, including hotels, restaurants, factory canteens, airlines, etc., all form a large and growing market.

Technical aspects such as grading and packaging are by agreement between the retailer and the supplier.

Wholesale markets

A wholesale market consists physically of a number of 'stands' either owned or rented by a particular wholesaler who buys or sells on commission. Usually a grower or his representing organisation consigns produce by prior arrangement with the wholesaler.

Samples of produce are usually placed on display and these, together with information on grading and the grower's 'mark', enable potential buyers to make purchasing decisions. The salesman will base his asking price on the state of supply and demand and, as he is paid on a commission basis he will attempt to get the highest price possible for the grower. It must, however, be appreciated that in dealing with a perishable product the need for rapid turnover will make a sale at any price necessary.

The primary wholesaler may be selling to secondary wholesalers who in turn will make their profit by marking up the original prices. There may be several such links in the chain between the grower and the consumer, although intense competition within the market will help to keep down excessive profit taking. The wholesale market in fact plays a crucial role in determining prices and standards.

To operate efficiently a wholesale market must be able to receive and despatch produce as rapidly as possible. The long established markets close to major population centres have been swallowed up by urban development and have become victims, and part of the cause of traffic congestion. Many markets have been rebuilt on more spacious and accessible sites on the outskirts of major cities. Mechanical handling facilities have also been improved to speed up throughput. A major source of increased efficiency stems from improved communications of market intelligence. Growers and buyers need market information in order to plan their activities. The telephone continues to play an important part in communicating information but the increasing use of the micro-computer, linked by telephone to a central computer will further increase the efficiency of marketing. For effective transfer of commodity information it is critical that the produce can be adequately defined. In the case of hard commodities such as gold there are few problems, definition becomes far more difficult when one considers the range of vegetables of different species and quality that can be considered. Grading standards are not new, the Emperor Diocletian, having fixed prices throughout the Roman Empire, found it necessary to lay down appropriate standards. However, stemming from the recommendations of a United Nations working party in 1955, international standards have been agreed upon for many vegetables. The European Economic Community, for example, has introduced statutory grading standards for a wide range of vegetable crops which must be adhered to when marketing through the wholesale market. The existence of statutory regulations necessitates a system for enforcement and government produce inspectors are an important component of the marketing organisation.

Auction markets

An alternative form of wholesale marketing is to sell produce to the highest bidder. An important variation of this method is the Dutch auction in which the price is gradually moved downwards, the first buyer to accept a price being the recipient. This method, which started in the Netherlands at the beginning of the century has now spread to other parts of Europe although not always successfully. The advantages of a Dutch auction over a conventional one are claimed to be:

- Greater speed of selling.
- Greater accuracy, with the electronic clock eliminating recording errors.
- Better prices for the grower that are a more accurate reflection of supply and demand.
- A greater honesty in trading since it is not possible for buyers to withhold bids by grouping or for growers' representatives to force the price up by fictitious bidding.

The Dutch Auction is more likely to operate successfully in situations where there are large quantities of standardised produce.

Export and import markets

The methods of marketing exported and imported vegetable crops are essentially the same as marketing home produce. Technicalities in trading agreements and tariffs are designed to protect the home producer and will often serve to complicate the transference of produce from one country to another so such marketing is usually carried out through a growers co-operative or marketing agent. The greater distances which are sometimes involved may have an effect on the method of transport and packaging and local grading regulations will have to be adhered to. Trade may also be influenced by the existence of plant health regulations devised to prevent the transfer of pests and diseases across international boundaries.

The processing market

Vegetables can be processed in many ways, each of which will have its different supply requirements. Invariably the emphasis is on quality and on continuity of supply so that processing machines can be used efficiently. Usually production areas are concentrated around the factories in order to reduce transport costs and delays which could result in produce deterioration. The principal methods of vegetable processing are freezing and canning, although there are smaller but important requirements for pickling and for dehydration. The production of vegetables for processing is a specialist operation as it is usually based on contractual agreements between the processor and the grower. The processor often provides technical advice to the grower and specifies the date of delivery of harvested produce to the factory. The processor will usually stipulate the choice of cultivar since some have characteristics which make them more suitable for the processing method to be used. For example, long-podded bean cultivars tend to have poor flavour and appearance when sliced for freezing and there are advantages in shorter-podded beans which can be harvested whole. In a similar way, small, dark green seeded peas are preferred for the freezing market. Cultivar choice is also important in relation to mechanisation and time of maturity.

Quality standards

All markets will have their own quality standards, some being more specific than others. In the U.K. the body responsible for maintaining quality standards of vegetables and other produce is the Horticultural Marketing Inspectorate (H.M.I.) which forms part of the national advisory service (A.D.A.S.). The standards currently in force differ in detail for individual species but are broadly as follows:

Extra Class – a luxury class which, though not applicable to all crops, frequently remains as a target quality.

Class I – the quality which forms the backbone of the industry and trade. Definition of the class will cover a number of attributes depending on the particular crop but those of size and the presence of blemishes and other damage figure among these. In the case of Brussels sprouts the class I category must be free from frost damage, whereas classes II and III allow for the presence of a limited amount of such damage. Bulb onions cannot be classed as I when they show signs of renewed growth although early signs of growth are permitted in up to 10% of the consignment in grade II and up to 20% in grade III.

Class II – a reasonable quality which has deficiencies of appearance but is eminently usable.

Class III – a quality which may not be in regular demand and frequently may be uneconomical to handle.

These qualities and descriptions are controlled at all stages of distribution following despatch from the grower right through until the retail stage. They do not, however, apply to sales to manufacturers for processing.

Quality in practice is a difficult parameter to describe and covers a number of characteristics. Grading standards place emphasis on visual appearance, for example size, colour and absence of visible defects. Flavour and texture are more difficult to assess but may form part of a contractual specification when supplying direct to a processor or a supermarket outlet, for example.

Previous chapters have dealt with the agronomy aspects of controlling quality attributes, such as size and freedom from disease. Stress has been placed on the role of plant spacing on size of produce, as from the marketing point of view this is well illustrated by the various outlets available for the carrot crop. Table 9.1. summarizes the size requirement for different uses in the carrot crop (Ministry of Agriculture, Fisheries and Food, 1980). Thus having established a market in advance a grower, making due allowance for variety and anticipated yield, will be able to adjust his plant population to provide him with a high proportion of roots in the required size bracket.

Table 9.1 Carrot size requirements for different purposes

Purpose	Shoulder diameter (mm)
Freezing	up to 26
Small roots for canning whole	19–32
Medium roots for canning whole	32–45
Prepacking	20–50
Loose packs for market	25–70
Large roots for slicing, dicing	over 45

Contract growing

From the view point of the processor some form of contract ensures a supply of raw material to keep his processing plant working. In a similar way large scale retailers and supermarkets must maintain turnover. The grower in turn wishes to secure some guarantee of actually selling his crop and also, if possible, knowing in advance what the future price is likely to be. A greater certainty of the market permits planning for the future.

There are various types of contract in terms of their reference to price:

- Fixed price contracts. The grower is assured an agreed price for his produce subject to it reaching the required specification. In this way the risk is tranferred from the grower to his customer.
- Cost plus contracts. The grower's cost of production is calculated and to this is added a margin for profit.
- Market price plus contracts. The grower in this situation is exposed to the variations in the market price resulting from changes in supply and demand. He does, however, provide benefits for producing superior quality crops.
- No price contracts. The grower in this case is exposed to the risks of changing prices but at least has the guarantee that his produce must be purchased.

The formulation of contracts in relation to the production of vegetables is difficult and escape mechanisms must be introduced to allow for inability to supply usually as a result of adverse weather conditions. Retail buyers will often prefer to base their purchasing on a 'gentleman's agreement'. Close technical liaison will often develop between purchaser and grower as a consequence of their interdependence.

Co-operatives

The process of negotiating with purchasers for better prices and contracts can be difficult for a small grower and is often done more effectively through marketing co-operatives. The latter are also able to integrate with other co-operatives and larger growers to place themselves jointly in a better bargaining position.

Marketing is a specialised task in the same way as crop production and many growers prefer to concentrate on the latter. A co-operative can thus handle all marketing aspects, often to the extent of running a packhouse or even investing in processing and retailing facilities. Member growers will of course have to pay for such services through a system of shares and levies.

Promoting produce can form an important function for a co-operative. For example, in many instances consumers may have a preference for imported vegetables over local produce. There are usually sound underlying reasons for such preferences. Until relatively recently, the British consumer favoured onions from abroad primarily because of their firmness and better appearance. Skin colour in particular was attractive and bulbs were less prone to rotting during storage. Research carried out was able to solve these problems, through a combination of seed treatment, direct harvesting and improved storage technology. These innovations, which have been referred to in previous chapters, were on their own, insufficient to dispel the consumer conviction that British onions were inferior to, for example, those imported from Spain. In order to improve the image of the British onion groups of growers coordinated their marketing and marketed high quality onions under their own brand name. By maintaining rigorous quality standards backed up by advertising it was possible to convince consumers that the brand was of superior quality and prices improved accordingly. There are many other examples where marketing has been coordinated in this manner to improve prices for the grower.

References and further reading

Arthey, V.D. (1975) *Quality of Horticultural Products*. London: Butterworth.

Bedford, L.V. (1980) 'Vegetable variety performance trials technique – assessment of colour, flavour and texture in processed vegetables'. *Journal of National Institute of Agricultural Botany*, **15**, 288–293.

Goodenough, P.W. and Atkin, R.K., eds (1981) *Quality in Stored and Processed Vegetables and Fruit*. London: Academic Press.

Joslyn, M.A. (1961) 'The freezing preservation of vegetables'. *Economic Botany*, **15**, 347–375.

Measures, J.K. (1976) 'Vegetables for processing – the grower's point of view: Brussels sprouts and cauliflowers'. In *Vegetables for Processing*. Bulletin 12. Scottish Horticultural Research Institute Association, pp. 9–14.

Ministry of Agriculture, Fisheries and Food (1980) *Carrots*. Booklet 2268. London: H.M.S.O.

Robinson, W.B., Wilson, D.E., Moyer, J.C., Atkin, J.D. and Hand, D.B. (1964) 'Quality versus yield of snap beans for processing'. *Proceedings of American Society of Horticultural Science*, **84**, 339–347.

Sargent, M.J. (1973) *Economics in Horticulture*. London: MacMillan.

Tanburn, J. (1981) *Food Distribution: As Impact on Marketing in the '80s*. London: Central Council for Agricultural and Horticultural co-operation.

Thompson, R. (1976) 'The agronomic problems of growing vegetables for specific outlets'. In *Vegetables for Processing*. Bulletin 12. Scottish Horticultural Research Institute Association, pp. 24–31.

10   Vegetable storage

Reasons for storing vegetables

There are many reasons for investing in storage facilities. The original reason for storing crops was, of course, to ensure a continual supply through seasons when fresh produce was unavailable. Nowadays it is possible to obtain almost any fresh vegetable throughout the year by importation from areas with more favourable climates. However, market prices reflect the availability of produce and cost of transportation, thus storage provides a method for extending the supply season in order to take advantage of the rising prices when supplies from the field are either non-existent or in short supply.

In some instances the price of produce may be determined by advance contracts with, for example processors, for delivery on agreed dates. Fluctuating weather conditions will generally prevent such precision planning and storage facilities will provide an essential buffer.

The provision of pre-packed vegetables to supermarket outlets is particularly difficult since both time of supply, and freshness of produce may both be precisely defined. In addition to fluctuations in seasonal demand, peak sales in most supermarkets usually take place on Thursdays and Fridays. The introduction of cool chain marketing by some outlets makes storage facilities essential for the grower since with this system produce is cooled immediately following harvest and must then be kept cool right up to the point of sale.

Marketing considerations are not the only reason for investing in storage facilities as there are other benefits. Labour organisation over the harvesting season is simplified as the farmer is more able to carry out operations at the optimum time. Harvesting during periods of favourable weather and when soil conditions are suitable will be more efficient and will generally result in better quality produce.

It is difficult to generalise on the technique for storing vegetables as storage can range from short term, for example a day in the case of lettuce, to long term for onions which may be stored throughout the entire winter and spring. The present chapter outlines the underlying principles of vegetable storage and surveys the available methods for providing storage facilities.

Storage physiology

The object of storage is to retain the product in a fresh state. Deterioration following harvest is caused by a number of factors but the principal ones are water loss and respiration. The rate of both of these processes is influenced by temperature and thus cooling is the basis of most storage methods. It is also important to store produce of high quality since infection by pest and diseases will often result in further deterioration which may not become obvious until the produce is removed for marketing.

Respiration rates differ between vegetables and are highest in the leafy salad crops that are actively growing at harvest time. Storage organs such as carrots and onions respire at much slower rates and will therefore remain fresh for much longer periods. Respiration rates are approximately halved by a 10°C drop in temperature and the aim should be to lower the temperature as soon after harvest as is economically practical. A leafy vegetable crop will often be harvested at temperatures in excess of the ambient and a few hours at summer temperatures may shorten the life of the produce by several days. Produce may deteriorate as much in an hour at 26°C as in a day at 12°C or a week at 1°C. Clearly, field heat must be removed rapidly to reduce losses in shelf life and to maintain the quality of the produce.

The amount of water that a crop can lose before it becomes unsaleable will vary with the species and also with varieties within a species (see table 10.1). Water loss will decrease as temperature is lowered and vapour pressure deficits are reduced. However, as the dew point is achieved free water will be deposited on the crop surface thus increasing the risk of rotting through fungal and bacterial infection.

Temperatures below freezing may cause damage through the formation of ice crystals within the plant tissue and, for this reason, most vegetable stores are operated at temperatures slightly above 0°C. However, some species of tropical origin, such as the tomato, aubergine and sweet potato, undergo chilling damage at tempera-

Table 10.1 Water loss at which vegetables become unsaleable

Vegetable	Maximum permissible loss (% of original weight)
Asparagus	8
Beans, broad	6
Beans, runner	5
Beetroot, storing	7
Beetroot, bunching with leaves	5
Broccoli	4
Brussels sprouts	8
Cabbage (different varieties)	7–10
Carrots, storing	8
Carrots, bunching with leaves	4
Cauliflower	7
Celery	10
Leeks	7
Lettuce	3–5
Onion	10
Parsnip	7
Potato	7
Peas (in pods)	5
Spinach	3
Sweet corn	7
Tomato	7
Turnip	5

tures well above zero resulting in chemical changes which may influence flavour adversely. In such instances storage should be maintained at higher temperatures depending on the particular crop. Tomatoes for example should not be cooled below 10°C. The extent of chilling injury depends on a number of factors including species, temperature and duration of exposure.

Although control of temperature and humidity is the basis of most vegetable storage it is also possible to slow down crop respiration by reducing the supply of oxygen to the plant cells, a principle adopted in controlled atmosphere storage. Some level of oxygen is essential since anaerobic conditions will lead to the production of alcohol and other products likely to alter the flavour.

Pre-storage treatment

Only clean, healthy plant material should be stored for prolonged periods if losses are to be avoided. Crops should be kept free from pests and diseases throughout their period of growth and harvesting methods and timing should be carried out in such a way as to minimise physical damage. Machine damaged carrots are, for example, susceptible to infection by air-borne spores *Botrytis cinerea* which can then spread through a store from root to root by contact. Other pathogens infecting wounds during carrot storage may include *Mycocentrospora acerina* and *Sclerotinia sclerotiorum*. Davies (1977) has demonstrated the possibility of wound healing prior to storage by keeping roots at 24–26°C at 98% relative humidity for a period of two days. A more common approach to reducing the incidence of rotting in many root vegetables is to use post-harvest, pre-storage dips of a broad spectrum fungicide such as benomyl. Similar treatment can also be used to reduce storage losses of Dutch white cabbage (Wale and Epton, 1981).

Disease infections can frequently occur long before the crop enters the store. Neck rot (*Botrytis allii*) of onions, which may cause serious storage losses, is a seed-borne disease to a large extent controllable by a fungicidal seed treatment of benomyl prior to sowing.

The reduction of onion sprouting during storage is achieved by spraying the crop with a sprout suppressant approximately two weeks prior to harvest. The compound used is maleic hydrazide although it has been shown experimentally that gamma irradiation of harvested bulbs may be more effective at suppressing growth, however this method is not employed commercially. Storage performance of onions can also be affected by stage of maturity at harvest (Tucker and Drew, 1982).

Field storage

Carrots and other root crops can often be kept for several months during the winter in the field *in situ* with some surface covering to prevent frost damage or alternatively in heaps or clamps similarly protected from frost. Field storage is by far the cheapest method of extending the supply period of such vegetables but cannot be continued into the spring when rising temperatures would lead to regrowth and other losses.

The simplest approach is to cover the crop once the foliage has died back with a layer of soil at least 15 cm deep or alternatively a 30 cm deep layer of loose straw to insulate the crop from possible frost damage. This technique is used principally for crops to be lifted from January onwards and can only be carried out on well drained sites.

A refinement on the above technique, which is suitable for storing most hardy root crops, is to stack the harvested roots in heaps which are then covered with a layer of straw or other insulating material. The clamps, as they are called, should generally measure no more than 1.5 m at their base and be of a similar height. Only sound roots should be stored in this way.

Field storage techniques are not solely applicable to root crops as celery has been stored in the field successfully for several weeks thus benefiting from the marked premium available during the early winter months (Whitlock, 1980). The season for outdoor celery usually ends when severe frost damages the petioles. It is possible to protect the standing crop from frost by covering with a layer of straw or other insulating material which is kept dry and held in place by a layer of polythene. Trials have demonstrated that white polythene keeps the crop in better condition than black polythene, probably by reflecting radiation and thus helping to keep down the temperature. The total area to be covered can be reduced by uprooting celery heads and placing them between rows of standing plants as illustrated in fig. 10.1. As in all forms of storage, the crop must be clean and free from disease to prevent the loss of crop under the covering. Covering should also be delayed until the weather is cool since warm conditions beneath the cover are conducive to disease spread.

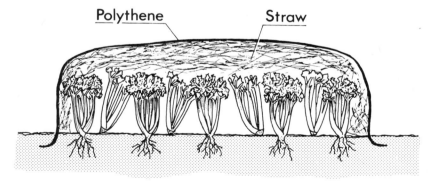

Fig. 10.1. Field storage of celery.

Controlled environment stores

The environment in a vegetable store can be controlled in a number of ways to prolong the life of produce, the principal one being to lower temperature in order to reduce respiration rates. Operating at cooler temperatures also reduces water loss by lowering the vapour pressure deficit. Some degree of humidity control may also be necessary to prevent excessive condensation on produce leading to spoilage. The store environment can also be controlled in terms of its atmospheric composition particularly with respect to oxygen content although this approach is usually used in association with cooling. In practice the use of controlled atmosphere stores is largely confined to fruit storage but their application to vegetables will be considered later in this chapter.

Ambient air stores

In temperate regions the cheapest way of lowering the temperature of a store is to make use of ambient air for cooling. By drawing external air into an insulated store during the night and early morning when temperatures are low it is possible to provide suitable conditions for storing vegetables during the winter. At other times of the year some form of refrigeration is necessary. Stores which use external air for cooling should ideally be controlled by a differential thermostat capable of both optimising the duration of ventilation and also preventing crop damage from temperatures below freezing. Ambient air stores are commonly used for overwinter storage of, for example, onions which are kept from autumn harvest through to the following spring.

Refrigerated cold stores

The majority of vegetable stores are cooled by some form of refrigeration. The following factors are important in the design and construction of cold stores:

- Adequate insulation is necessary to prevent undue heat gain during warm weather which would result in increasing the refrigeration capacity requirement and running costs. Careful design is essential to prevent condensation within the insulation material.
- Refrigeration capacity must be sufficient to cope with peak cooling requirements. In practice the cooling requirement in a

well insulated store is mainly required to rapidly remove field heat from produce following harvest. Refrigeration capacity can be reduced considerably if field heat is removed in a separate operation.

- Air distribution is important to ensure even distribution of low temperatures throughout the store. Failure in this respect can led to localised crop deterioration as a consequence of either condensation or the development of hot spots.
- Instrumentation is critical to the efficient operation of any store and the location of temperature and humidity sensors is particularly important. As in all areas of environmental control, computers are playing an increasingly important role in store management.

Removal of field heat

It is particularly important in the case of leafy vegetables harvested during warm weather to carry out cooling as quickly as possible following harvest. A conventional cold store is unsuited for this operation for as much as three quarters of the refrigerator capacity may be required simply to remove field heat and cooling rates are frequently no better than 0.5°C per hour. There have been a number of developments to overcome this problem.

Hydro cooling

In this method vegetables are either immersed or sprayed with cooled water. The efficiency of this technique depends on the large heat transfer coefficient between cooling water and the crop surface. The process removes no water from the crop but the remaining surface wetness can lead to crop deterioration. There is also a risk of contamination by bacteria and fungi in the cooling water although this can be minimised by the introduction of chlorine and other disinfectants. The main advantage of the technique is that it is rapid, taking between ten and twenty minutes per batch.

Vacuum cooling

Evaporative cooling is achieved by placing produce in a chamber from which air is evacuated to produce a partial vacuum. Water evaporates from the surface of the produce as the pressure is reduced and in doing so extracts the latent heat of evaporation.

Vacuum coolers capable of standing an external load of one atmosphere are available to vegetable growers and have been used successfully, particularly by lettuce growers, although the technique is suitable for most leafy vegetables having a relatively high surface area. Cooling time is rapid being in the order of twenty minutes per batch. Increased efficiency of vacuum coolers has been achieved by introducing cooling coils into the chambers to condense water vapour derived from the produce. Unless the crop surface is wet there is a slight loss in fresh weight amounting to 1% for each 5.6°C drop in temperature.

Ice bank coolers

A major problem with the conventional refrigerated store is that a high proportion of the refrigerator capacity is used to remove field heat. In the absence of pre-cooling techniques such as those described above it would be necessary to have uneconomically large refrigeration units in order to cope with peak demands in cooling requirements. This irregular demand can be evened out by using the ice bank cooler in which a relatively small refrigeration unit is used to produce a large block of ice. Water surrounds the ice and is circulated through a cooling tower which in turn cools and humidifies a counter flow of air drawn from the store (see fig. 10.2). In this way rapid cooling is achieved when required, the ice block growing when demand for cooling is low and melting down during periods of peak demand. Temperature control is relatively simple since the cooling water cannot drop below 0°C and the produce cannot therefore suffer from freezing damage. Water loss from produce is also minimised by the high humidity produced by this type of cooling.

Cool chain marketing

In cool chain marketing, produce is kept continually cool from the time when field heat is removed following harvest right through until it is purchased by the consumer. This form of marketing ensures that produce reaches the consumer in near perfect condition although this is achieved at a cost. It is particularly suitable for salad crops which deteriorate rapidly at ambient temperatures.

Refrigerated transport forms an important link between the farm cold store and the store's chilled counter display area at the point of sale. Normally produce will also pass through a distribution centre

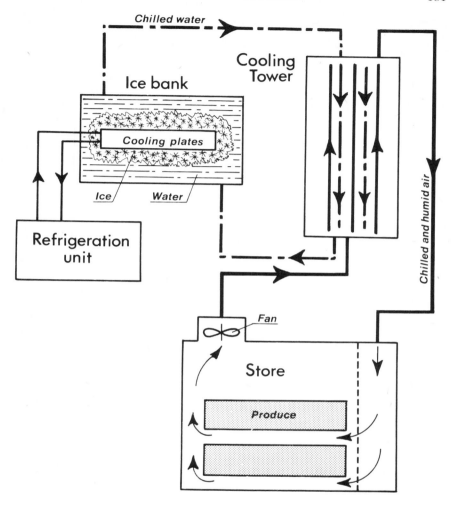

Fig. 10.2. Diagrammatic representation of the Ice Bank Cooler.

where it will be reconsigned to different destinations together with produce from other growers. During the entire period it must be maintained at the appropriate temperature and humidity level. Refrigerated road transport is usually designed to hold produce at a low temperature and may not be capable of lowering temperatures rapidly from ambient levels. The initial pre-cooling must therefore be conducted at the farm level. Any break in the chain risks the development of condensation together with an increase in the risk of product deterioration.

Controlled atmosphere storage

Respiratory rates of crop produce are reduced by storing in gas-tight chambers under reduced oxygen and increased carbon dioxide concentrations. The carbon dioxide has the additional beneficial effect of slowing down the growth of micro-organisms and also reducing the loss of chlorophyll which occurs during the senescence of leafy vegetables. High carbon dioxide levels have also been shown to improve tenderness of asparagus and broccoli stored under conditions of controlled atmosphere, (Dennis, 1981).

Although extensively used for fruit, controlled atmosphere storage has not been widely accepted for extending the life of vegetables. This may in part be due to the very specific and differing conditions required for different crop species and even for different cultivars of the same species. The requirements for different vegetable crops have been reviewed in detail by Isenberg (1979).

Low pressure or hypobaric storage

In many respects low pressure storage is similar to controlled atmospheric storage. By reducing store pressure to one tenth of atmospheric, oxygen levels are correspondingly lowered and respiration rates are reduced. This technique has the advantage that naturally produced gases such as ethylene do not accumulate in plant tissues and it is particularly attractive for the storage of tomatoes where chilling injury will occur under conventional cold storage. Lougheed *et al.* (1978) have reviewed the use of low pressure storage for horticultural crops.

Irradiation

The storage life of many vegetables can be prolonged following gamma irradiation treatment, but development of this method is not likely to be possible because of the high capital cost and seasonal nature of crop production.

Storage of different vegetables together

Although as a general principle produce life may be extended by storage at low temperatures and high humidities, practical problems may arise when a grower wishes to store different vegetables in a single store. In practice three sets of storage conditions will cope with the majority of vegetables.

● *Low temperature/high humidity (0–1°C; 90–95% R.H.)*
This range is suitable for a wide variety of crops including the following:

Asparagus	Lettuce	Rhubarb
Beet	Mushrooms	Salad onions
Brassicas	Parsnips	Spinach
Celery	Peas	Sweet corn
Leeks	Radishes	Turnips

● *Low temperatures/low humidity (0–1°C; 60–65% R.H.)*
This setting is more appropriate for long-term storage of bulb onions.

● *High temperature/high humidity (13°C; 90–95% R.H.)*
This high setting will prevent chilling damage to many crops of tropical origin including the following:

Beans (Runner and French)	Early Potatoes
Cucumber	Tomatoes
Melons	

Where compromise is essential then the high temperature and high humidity store will produce the least damage to produce.

Problems can sometimes occur through tainting of one crop by another. Ethylene production for example by ripe tomatoes can also affect green vegetables causing bleaching and increased incidence to rotting. Packaging can help to reduce the extent of the problem although if it is serious then separate stores are the only realistic alternative.

References and further reading

Davies, W.P. (1977) 'Infection of carrot roots in cool storage by *Centrospora acerina*'. *Annals of applied Biology*, **85**, 163–164.

Dennis, C. (1981) 'The effect of storage conditions on the quality of vegetables and salad crops'. In *Quality in Stored and Processed Vegetables and Fruit*, eds. P.W. Goodenough and R.K. Atkin, London: Academic Press, pp. 329–339.

Electricity Council (1974) *Vegetable Storage*. Farm Electric Handbook No. 23, Kenilworth, Warwickshire.

Goodenough, P.W. and Atkin, R.K. eds. (1981) *Quality in Stored and Processed Vegetables and Fruit*. London: Academic Press.

Isenberg, F.M.R. (1979) 'Controlled atmospheric storage of vegetables'. *Horticultural Reviews*, **1**, 337–394.

Lindsay, R.T. and Neale, M.A. (1981) 'Cold stores for fresh vegetables'. In *Quality in Stored and Processed Vegetables and Fruit*, eds. P.W. Goodenough and R.K. Atkin, London: Academic Press, pp. 315–328.

Lougheed, E.C., Murr, D.P. and Berard, L. (1978) 'Low pressure storage for horticultural crops'. *Hortscience*, **13**, 21–27.

Robinson, J.E., Browne, K.M. and Burton, W.G. (1975) 'Storage characteristics of some vegetables and soft fruits'. *Annals of Applied Biology*, **81**, 399–408.

Tucker, W.G. and Drew, R.L.K. (1982) 'Post-harvest studies on autumn-drilled bulb onions. The effect of harvest date, conditioning treatments and field drying on skin quality and storge performance'. *Journal of Horticultural Science*, **57**, 339–348.

Wale, S.J. and Epton, A.S. (1981) 'The effect of field nitrogen and post-harvest fungicide dips on storge of Dutch white cabbage'. In *Quality in stored and Processed Vegetables and Fruit*. eds. P.W. Goodenough and R.K. Atkin, London: Academic Press, pp. 301–312.

Whitlock, A.J. (1980) 'Low cost vegetable storage'. *Arthur Rickwood Experimental Husbandry Farm, Annual Review*, Mepal, Cambridgeshire, 23–27.

11 Machinery for vegetable growing

During the past thirty years the developed countries of the world have experienced a revolution in vegetable production techniques as a result of mechanisation. Crops which were traditionally grown intensively on small areas of land with large inputs of labour are now produced on large, highly mechanised farms. The onion crop, for example, is now mainly in the hands of large-scale farmers. Other vegetable crops, such as runner beans, are less amenable to handling by existing machines although research and development are likely to overcome such difficulties in time. Economic and social factors must ultimately decide the level of mechanisation used in the production of specific vegetables but, in spite of the increasing cost of fuel, it is likely that vegetable production will become increasingly dependent on the use of machines.

The development of suitable machinery for vegetable production has not been carried out in isolation by the agricultural engineer. He has been aided by the plant breeder who has bred cultivars of many of our vegetables that for one reason or another have been more suited to mechanical treatment. The work of the breeder has been particularly important in connection with harvesting. Similarly the agronomist has been able to manipulate growing systems to tie in with the constraints of mechanisation. The development of bed systems of production is a consequence of collaboration between agronomists and engineers. The future progress of mechanisation of vegetable production must rely more and more on the work of multi-disciplinary teams of specialists.

This chapter does not set out to review in detail the entire range of machinery available to the vegetable grower but to indicate the principal types of equipment in relation to their use on the farm. Where appropriate, reference is also made to recent trends in the development of machinery for use in vegetable production.

Cultivating

Land cultivation prior to crop establishment is usually considered under the headings of primary cultivation, in which initial preparation of the topsoil is carried out, followed by secondary cultivation aimed at improving the tilth of the surface layers prior to sowing or planting.

Primary cultivation

The mould board plough continues to be the main tool for carrying out primary cultivation. By its action of inverting the soil it buries weeds and crop residues thus facilitating the use of machinery for subsequent cultivations. By throwing the soil surface into furrows it will improve water infiltration into the soil and assist the process of weathering to improve the surface tilth. The basic principle of the plough has changed little, developments being associated with the increased power of tractors which have made it possible to increase the number of furrows turned in one pass. The development of the reversible plough has also increased the rate of ploughing by reducing unnecessary travel. It also has the advantage of producing a more level field thus facilitating subsequent mechanical operations.

Secondary cultivation

The purpose of secondary cultivation is to break down the furrowed surface left by ploughing to form a level surface of suitable tilth for either seed sowing or transplanting. A large range of equipment has been developed for this purpose, the choice of which will be affected in part by soil type and conditions, etc.

Cultivators

There are many types of cultivators for use after ploughing and some of the heavier versions are classified as *chisel ploughs* and can be used for primary cultivation. All consist of a series of tines or spikes which can be drawn through the soil behind a tractor thus breaking clods into small particles. Angling of the tines ensures that lumps are brought to the surface. The basic form has *rigid tines* but *spring loaded tine cultivators* are more suited to strong ground since the tines will spring back to prevent damage by obstructions. A further variation uses tines made from spring steel and is therefore referred to as a *spring tine cultivator*. In addition to being less vulnerable to damage than the rigid type, spring tines tend to vibrate as they move through the soil thus increasing the shattering effect on clods.

It is usual to make at least two passes with a cultivator, the first at right angles to the furrows left by ploughing and the second parallel to the original furrows. The forward speed of the tractor, tine design and spacing, and the depth adjustment all influence the effect and ability of the cultivator to break down the soil left by the plough. The depth of cultivation will depend on many factors including previous ploughing depth, soil type, intended crop, etc. The addition of a levelling board in front and levelling combs or rotary crumblers behind the tined cultivator also aid in producing level seedbeds and reduce the number of passes necessary to complete the operation.

Cultivators can normally be operated over the depth range 10 to 60 cm although 20 to 30 cm is more usual.

Harrows

Harrows are similar in principle to the tined cultivators but are used as a follow up to produce an even finer tilth. They consist of tines mounted on frames, a number of which can be pulled behind a single tractor. Their depth of operation is about 15 cm and in addition to their effect on producing a finer tilth they also serve to level the soil. As with cultivators the tine may be either rigid or sprung. In the case of *chain harrows* the mounted tines are substituted by a mat of interconnecting chain links whose primary function is to produce a very fine, level surfaced seedbed.

Disc harrows

These consist of a series of concave discs mounted on a shaft, referred to as a 'gang', a number of which may be drawn behind a tractor. Soil is thrown up by the leading gang and drawn back by the following one. The discs rotate as a result of the forward motion through the soil, thus breaking clods by a cutting motion rather than impact as with tines. Slight angling of the mounting shaft increases both penetration and the throwing action of the discs. They have a working depth of about 15 cm and can be adjusted by altering the angle between the gangs to a maximum of about 25°. They are often used in preference to tined cultivation when there is a great deal of surface trash.

Rollers

The final stage of producing level seedbed free of remaining soil clods can be achieved using a roller drawn behind a tractor. They are particularly useful in firming loose or puffy seedbeds especially when conditions are dry.The Cambridge roll or ring roller, made from a series of iron rings mounted on a shaft, is usually suitable for vegetable production.

Rotary cultivators

The implements discussed so far have all derived their energy from their forward movement as a result of being pulled by tractors. Given suitable weather conditions and the skill and judgement of the grower they are capable, in combination, of producing good conditions for subsequent seed sowing or transplanting. However, in modern vegetable production schedules it is not always feasible to wait for the 'right' conditions and it is frequently necessary to 'force a tilth'. This invariably requires the use of some form of powered cultivator of which the rotary cultivator is the most common basic form. Although designs vary, they normally consist of a series of 'L' shaped blades mounted on a rotating shaft driven from the power-take-off at the tractor. Appropriate choice of rotor speed and depth together with the forward speed of the tractor all serve to control the degree of soil cultivation. It should, however, be appreciated that this increased ability to produce a seedbed brings with it considerable scope for misuse and there is a danger of over cultivation leading to a breakdown of soil structure.

Subsoilers and pan busters

The importance of good soil drainage has been emphasised in earlier chapters but frequent use of heavy machinery, particularly on the heavier textured soils, causes compaction and impedes water movement. The development of panning as a consequence of ploughing or cultivating to the same depth too often will also prevent the free flow of water through the soil profile. The problem can be minimised by, for example, using lighter machines or by reducing the number of passes needed to complete the operation. Similar results may be achieved by using cage wheels, double wheels and balloon tyres to spread the load of machinery. The formation of a plough pan will also be prevented if the plough depth is varied between cultivations.

Various forms of subsoilers are available, usually consisting of heavy duty machines, having a working depth of between 40 and 60 cm. Some are fitted with horizontal 'wings' which help shatter the compacted subsoil without bringing it to the surface.

Pan busters typically have three or five tines inclined forward to aid penetration. They need heavy tractors and are used to rip soil in advance of ploughing or cultivation. The use of heavy equipment in itself contributes to compaction so passes with subsoilers and pan busters must be kept to a minimum.

Spading machines

The spading machine, which simulates the effect of manual digging, is a modified form of the rotary cultivator in which the blades are spade shaped and in addition to rotating in a forward direction they also turn the soil. They have the disadvantage of a low work rate due to a low forward speed but they have been found particularly useful in cultivating silt land. Both spading machines and rotary cultivators can be used for primary cultivation, thus substituting for the traditional plough.

Reciprocating harrow

In this form of harrow the vertical harrow spikes are mounted on bars that are oscillated sideways at up to 500 cycles per minute.

Rotary harrows

The powered rotary harrow is made up from pairs of gear driven rotors, contra-rotating about a vertical axis moving at up to 250–300 r.p.m. Working depths are anything up to 25 cm and they are useful for producing a rapid tilth but have a tendency to bring stones and clods to the surface.

Other equipment used for primary and secondary cultivation

The machinery described so far in this section covers the principal techniques for producing suitable seedbeds. Many modifications exist to improve the efficiency of soil machinery and refinements such as levelling combs and anti-ridging boards help to perfect the final stages of soil preparation prior to crop establishment. Other items of equipment of use to the vegetable producer are:

Stone breakers and pickers
Stones can be a particular problem in land used for growing root vegetables such as carrots and onions and generally speaking it is better to avoid stony ground for these crops. Depending on the size and hardness of stones it is possible to use machinery to either break them down or alternatively to pick them up for transport to a disposal site. Stone pickers are similar in design to potato harvesters.

Double diggers
In the early days of market gardens it was common practice to double dig the soil by removing a spit of soil to produce a narrow trench which thus permitted the cultivation of a strip of subsoil before covering it with the next spit of topsoil. In this way both topsoil and subsoil could be dug without reversing the order of the two layers. It was also common practice to incorporate organic matter into the subsoil during the operation, thus improving the soil structure to a depth of 50 cm or more. Machinery is under development at Wye College, in Kent, which simulates this process and tests with a prototype Wye Double Digger have demonstrated the potential benefits of such machinery for vegetable production.

Bed makers
The use of bed systems for reducing the dangers of soil compaction have already been referred to. Depending on the soil type, significant reductions in yield can arise from previous wheeltracks if these coincide with the cropped area. Whatever system of bed making is employed it is important to create wheelings directly following primary cultivation and to keep to them for all subsequent operations. The restricted area of compaction can then either be broken at the end of the season by means of a winged tine running down the wheelings or alternatively the beds can be retained on a more permanent basis when the wheelings can remain compacted.

Bed making machinery itself consists essentially of a normal rotary type cultivator of appropriate width behind which is mounted a hood designed to produce the final bed shape. Bed designs vary in detail and may be either flat topped or curved in cross-section to aid in water removal and to some extent in soil warming.

Seeding

The importance of plant populations and synchronous seedling emergence in determining the size and uniformity of many vegetable species has been stressed in chapter 5. Various types of precision drill make it possible to sow seed at accurately spaced positions although it is still not possible to guarantee that each seed will germinate. Greater precision in drilling may be achieved by using either graded seed or, in the case of non spherical seed such as carrot, by using pelleted seed.

Various systems of seed metering are available to ensure accurate placement of seed. Cell wheel feed units consist of interchangeable wheels divided into cells in which seeds are isolated before release and a range of wheel sizes is available for different seeds and spacing. Belt feed systems are based on a similar principle, having interchangeable belts which may contain up to three lines of feed holes.

Other types include cup feed systems where individual seeds are picked up by cups attached to the circumference of a wheel. A more recent development is that of the vacuum drill, in which individual seeds are held against holes in a metering disc by a partial vacuum which when broken releases the seed. Benefits of this method include the possibility of using irregularly shaped natural seed and also the ability to drill at higher speeds.

The development of the fluid drilling technique of establishing pre-germinated seeds has necessitated the design of special fluid drills capable of extruding the seed-containing carrier gel into the soil. The fluid drills available at present operate by means of a peristaltic pump which forces blobs of gel into the furrow at a spacing related to the forward movement of the drill. This method has the advantage that the positive pressures required to force out the gel ensures that the outlet does not become blocked by soil, which is a potential problem with other types of drill when soil conditions are slightly sticky. However, it is difficult to ensure that a single germinated seed is present in each blob of gel thus reducing the degree of precision spacing.

Transplanting

The development of transplanting systems depends on a close integration between the propagation and planting stages of the operation. The various techniques of plant raising were referred to in chapter 5 and a range of machinery has been introduced to handle the different types of plant.

Transplanting bare-root material

The types of machine available for planting bare-rooted transplants are usually hand fed but part of the process can be mechanised to increase output. Operators sit on low seats on the tractor-mounted planter and drop each plant directly into a furrow which is then closed by a pair of press wheels. Speeds are slow and will usually be 1–2 km/h depending on spacing within the row. Planters differ in the number of rows they can handle in one pass but typically consist of two-row systems with one person planting each row and a third handing plants to them. Modifications permit operators to place plants into various transfer devices on an endless conveyor, following which the remainder of the planting operation is automated. The operation is thus simplified and planting rates can be increased.

In the methods outlined above the bare-rooted plants are introduced into a furrow opened by a share and closed by inclined press wheels. This approach is often used for brassica transplants but the principle is equally applicable to a wide range of species raised in peat blocks. An alternative system, particularly favoured by leek growers, is to drop plants into holes made in advance by a tractor-mounted mechanical dibber.

Automatic transplanting

Bare-rooted transplants do not lend themselves to mechanical handling and developments in automatic planting have proceeded with development of plant raising in peat blocks and other systems designed to produce plants rooted within their own discrete units of compost. For example, some machines can be fed manually by dropping the modules, root first, down chutes which direct the plant into an open furrow. By such methods it is possible to speed up planting rates from 1500 plants per operator hour on the manually fed machines used for bare-root material to a rate in the region of 4500 plants per operator hour.

The development of fully automatic machinery capable of handling 15 000 or more plants per operator hour has necessitated the development of specialist plant raising techniques. For example, the system designed by engineers at the National Institute of Agricultural Engineers, in the U.K., uses a bandolier of linked cylindrical peat blocks in which the plants are raised. This is then fed automatically to the planting machine which cuts the bandolier into separate blocks for delivery between two parallel, descending belts to the soil.

The Techniculture system developed in the U.S.A. uses a small cylindrical plug of compost impregnated with a binding agent as its basis for plant raising and automatic transplanting. Synchronised rods push rows of transplants into a special designed belt from which they are individually plucked prior to high speed planting.

Spraying machinery

Crop spraying is carried out for a number of reasons but principally in connection with protection from weeds, pests and diseases. Other applications may include foliar feeding of micro-nutrients and haulm destruction prior to harvesting. The rates of application used are divided into rather arbitrary divisions based on the volume of material applied:

Low volume	50–200	litres per hectare
Medium volume	200–700	litres per hectare
High volume	700 +	litres per hectare

In each case the amount of active chemical ingredient in the spray is adjusted to give an approximate dose per hectare. In low volume spraying the droplet size is usually small and individual droplets adhere to the crop surface in individual specks. A more complete crop cover is achieved at the higher volumes which may be an important consideration particularly for use in dense canopy situations. The principal advantage of low volume spraying is that as less water is required, lighter machinery can be used thus reducing soil compaction, and savings in both energy use and time can be achieved. Ultralow volume (ULV) spraying in which application rates are in the order of 5 litres per hectare may be applicable in some situations.

Machines can either be specifically designed for the spraying rates or for a more universal range extending from low to high volume application. This is usually achieved in practice by adjustment of pump pressures and changing nozzle sizes.

Various boom widths are available to suit different conditions and for use in Brussels sprouts, for example, may be fitted with row crop droppers which enable spray to be directed sideways into the crop. Band sprayers are also available which enable chemicals to be applied to rows of crops in a narrow strip, thus saving on costs.

Other crop protection equipment

Although not widely used by vegetable growers, fungicides and insecticides can be applied as dusts. The method has the advantage that it dispenses completely with water transport but can only be carried out effectively at low wind velocity. Tractor-mounted dusting machinery uses a blower which may either be operated from the tractor's power take-off or a separate small petrol engine.

A more widespread method for applying chemicals in vegetable growing is by granular application. Several systemic insecticides and a few herbicides can be applied in this way, either by incorporation into the soil at sowing or as surface bands along the crop rows. The simplest equipment for these types of application is similar to a space drilling unit fitted with an agitator, force feed and adjustable delivery spouts.

Irrigation equipment

The systems favoured by most vegetable growers are either based on oscillating spray lines or small to medium rotary sprinklers. Factors governing the choice were dealt with in chapter 7, in which the importance of infiltration rates and other soil characteristics were discussed.

Oscillating spray lines normally consist of 30–50 mm diameter pipes supported on light steel frames and having jets approximately every 0.6 m along the line. Most are fitted with a hydraulic pump at the end which oscillates the line through an angle of about 90°. The line is made up of typically 5 m lengths, the total overall operating length depending to a large extent on the delivery capacity of the pump.

Sprinkler irrigation systems offer a number of advantages over spray lines. They are capable of applying water at high rates and because of their larger droplet size they can throw water a larger distance. Although they apply water in the form of a circle compared with the rectangular application from spray lines, by overlapping the output from adjacent sprinklers a reasonably uniform application pattern can be achieved. Sprinklers most commonly used are slow rotating (approximately 1 revolution per minute) and cover a circle of 18–30 m in diameter. Rain guns having a much larger throw are less suited to vegetable production since they produce large size droplets which can cause damage to both crops and soil.

Most of the labour requirement for irrigation is necessary for moving delivery pipes and sprinklers onto new areas. Much of this can be avoided by using various forms of mobile equipment. The most popular method used by vegetable growers consists of self travelling sprinklers which can irrigate large areas of approximately rectangular field space with very little requirement for labour. Systems vary but usually consist of a sprinkler or boom mounted either on a skid or on wheels, enabling it to be drawn across a field. Movement is effected by the gradual automatic rewinding of the flexible delivery hose onto a stationary reel.

Harvesting

Harvesting is still one of the most labour intensive operations in the production of vegetables, although major developments continue to improve the capabilities of machines to replace man in this area.

Potato harvesters have now reached an advanced stage of development in which the crop can be lifted, cleaned and sorted ready for delivery to the store by a single machine. Stones and clods can be removed by electronic separators which use X-ray sources to detect their higher resistance relative to that of the potatoes. The extension of potato harvesting systems to operate on other root crops, such as carrots, is relatively easy and multi-purpose digger elevator harvesters are available to growers. Various sizes of machine exist and it is possible to lift a full bed width in one pass.

Most other machinery available for harvesting is crop specific. The harvesting of peas for processing, for example, has become an extremely specialised operation necessitating the use of very sophisticated harvesting machinery. Modern mobile pea viners separate and clean peas in a single pass, harvesting quantities in the order of 2 tonnes per hour. Such machinery can also be used for harvesting broad beans.

Dwarf green bean harvesters are also commercially available in a number of different designs. Beans are separated from the plants without cutting or uprooting them, by means of spring-steel fingers.

A range of equipment is available for use in the mechanised harvesting of Brussels sprouts. There are basically three designs of mechanism for stripping sprouts from pre-cut stems. Two of these involve manually feeding the stems through circular stripping devices made of either small vibrating knives or alternatively by a series of rotating knives which encircle the stem. The third method mechanically harvests stems following deleafing before passing them through a unit which rubs the sprouts off by rotation against a series of static serrated bars and rubber beaters. Facilities also exist for cleaning the sprouts before discharging them into bulk handling facilities prior to removal from the field.

A prerequisite for most mechanical harvesting techniques is that the crop should mature uniformly thus permitting a single pass operation. Although sensing devices have been developed which enable crops to be individually assessed, in most instances where a multi-stage harvest is necessary the human eye and touch are better at maintaining quality control. This is particularly so for crops such as crisp lettuce and calabrese (broccoli) to be marketed as pre-packs, for which particularly high quality is usually demanded. The development of machinery in this area has hinged around mobile packing units which are usually built round tractors. Manually harvested crops are placed onto wing conveyors which carry them into the main platform of the machine where any further trimming and grading is carried out prior to packing.

Gantry systems

The use of mobile gantry systems in the production of high value glasshouse crops is becoming increasingly common. Various designs are in use, many of which will, in addition to transporting workers over the crop, carry out operations such as irrigation and fertiliser application. By straddling the crop they obviate the need for pathways, thus increasing the production area. Although their current use in relation to field vegetable growing is largely confined to the glasshouse production of modular transplants they also have an application to field scale use. One Swiss designed gantry system (Lawson, 1982), for example, has a 21 m span, the bottom of which is approximately 2.5 m above ground level. It is supported at each end on driving wheels which run on 80 cm wide tracks. When the machine reaches the end of a bed the wheels can be turned through 90 degrees so that the entire structure can be driven sideways until lined up with the adjacent bed. A number of operations can be carried out from a working platform suspended below the gantry. For example, a team of twelve operators can plant or harvest lettuce, each being responsible for a strip of land corresponding to the more conventional bed width. It is not difficult to envisage further developments leading to an almost completely automatic cropping system.

References and further reading

Culpin, C. (1981) *Farm Machinery* 10th edn. London: Granada Publishing.

Darter, I.E. (1981) 'Trends in application technology'. *Outlook on Agriculture*, **10**, 319–320.

Hawker, M.F.J. and Keenlyside (1977) *Horticultural Machinery* 2nd edn. London: Longmans.

Lawson, G. (October 1982) 'Swiss field 70 ft. gantry'. *Grower*, 22–24.

Ministry of Agriculture, Fisheries and Food (1979) *Brussels Sprouts*. Reference Book 323, London: H.M.S.O.

Ministry of Agriculture, Fisheries and Food (1981) *Propagating and Transplanting Vegetables*. Reference Book 344, London: H.M.S.O.

Robertson, J. (1974) *Mechanising Vegetable Production*. Ipswich, Suffolk: Farming Press.

Warboys, I.B., Gooderham, P.T. and Wilkes, J.M. (1979) 'The incorporation of fertilisers into sub-soil by the Wye Double Digger'. *Proceedings of the International Soil Tillage Research Organisation*. University of Hohenheim, **2**, 315–320.

12   Vegetable seed production

With the exception of a small number of species that are propagated vegetatively, the majority of vegetable crops are grown from seed. The production of good quality seed is therefore an important prerequisite to successful vegetable growing. The present chapter outlines the sequence of events involved in production of vegetable seed, ranging from the initial development of a new variety through to the final marketing of commercial quantities to the grower.

Natural seed production

Seed production results from the fusion of the male nucleus in pollen with a female nucleus in the ovule. If the male and female nuclei are from the same plant then the resultant progeny constitute what is known as a *pure line*. Members of a pure line are not necessarily genetically identical although they are likely to be far more uniform than those arising from cross-pollination. In this process of self-pollination the resulting seed is said to be true to type. However, in many species mechanisms have evolved to encourage cross-pollination or out-breeding in which pollen transfer takes place between plants thus producing seed combining attributes of both male and female parent. In the case of dioecious plants, for example asparagus and spinach, the male and female flowers occur on separate plants making cross-pollination obligatory.

The distinction between self-pollinated and cross-pollinated plants is not absolute and to some extent species will often operate on both systems, although usually one or the other will predominate. In table 12.1 the more important vegetable crops are classified on the basis of their normal method of pollination.

These two broad groupings will not only influence the method used by the plant breeder to produce new cultivars but will also determine the method of commercial seed production.

Table 12.1 Principal form of pollination in common vegetable species

Normally self-pollinated	Normally cross-pollinated
Aubergine	Brassicas
French bean	Broad bean
Leek	Carrot
Lettuce	Celery
Peas	Maize
Pepper	Marrow
Tomato	Onion
	Parsnip
	Runner bean

Production of new cultivars

The plant breeder sets out to produce new cultivars with many different objectives. Yield and disease resistance are two of the most commonly sought after characteristics but suitability for mechanical harvesting and flavour are two examples of attributes that have taken on greater importance in recent years.

The plant breeder's objective is to combine desirable genetic attributes from all available resources into a single new cultivar. The starting point for any new breeding programme is thus to establish a 'germplasm' collection containing a wide range of genetic variability available within the species. The collection is likely to contain not only existing cultivars but also their wild progenitors. Both natural and induced mutations are additional sources of potentially useful variations. In recent years there has been an increasing awareness of the importance of maintaining genetic resources and steps have been taken to establish gene banks where long term storage can be maintained. A vegetable gene bank was established at the National Vegetable Research Station, in the U.K., during 1980 (Astley and Lockett, 1981), in which seeds are stored under conditions of low temperature and humidity for distribution to breeders throughout the world. Seed stocks are periodically checked for viability and reproduced as necessary.

The main technique available to the breeder for producing new genotypes is to hybridise parents of different genetic make-up by a process of cross-pollination. In some instances successful cross-pollination may be prevented by incompatibility mechanisms and special techniques may be needed to overcome such problems. The details of genetics and plant breeding techniques are beyond the scope of the present volume but the following paragraphs outline some of the methods commonly used.

Mass selection

Mass selection is more appropriate to cross-pollinated plants where variability is likely to be more pronounced. In this method the aim is to select the most desirable plants in the population and transfer them to an isolated site for future seed production. The proportion of the crop selected in this way may vary widely but typically is in the order of 10% or less of the total population.

Selected plants are seeded together and the seed harvested in bulk thus combining numerous genotypes, the mean performance of which should be an improvement upon the original population.

Roguing

The process of roguing is more useful in maintaining the standard of a cultivar rather than improving it. Plants that show undesirable traits are removed from the total population, leaving the more typical plants to grow on and produce seed.

Single plant selection

Self-pollinated cultivars usually show little genetic variation. However, particularly in the case of older examples, the total population may consist of numerous homozygous pure lines in single plant selection; individual plants showing desirable characteristics are selected and grown on separately to produce several parallel pure lines which may include promising new cultivars.

Hybridisation

Using the above methods of selection the breeder is confined to the limited variability available in existing populations. The objective of hydridisation is to generate increased variability in the hope of obtaining new and desirable combinations of heritable characters.

In the case of normally self-pollinated plants, initial crosses are carried out to produce the first, or F_1 generation. This uniform F_1 generation can then be self-pollinated with the result that the following F_2 generation will be made up of progeny containing a range of characters from each of the original parents. Alternatively, further variability can be introduced by crossing an F_1 generation with a third parent to bring in other desirable characteristics. If the breeder wishes to recover a greater proportion of the genetic constitution from one of the original parents this can be achieved through a series of back crosses to this parent. From the progeny of such crosses it is possible, over a number of generations, to select new cultivars which will breed true. Generally between five and six generations of inbreeding are sufficient to fix most characters.

There are variations on the above method. The so called pedigree method keeps the seed from each plant in the F_2 generation separate in order to take advantage of any homozygosity that may have appeared by the third generation. In this method of breeding many lines are rejected in each generation.

In contrast the bulk method consists of growing all material from the F_1 generation in a single plot until about the F_6 generation, when selection is carried out. By this time many uniform lines will have been produced and individual plants can be selected for testing. Some of the more undesirable characteristics may also have been eliminated by the process of natural selection.

The production and maintenance of varieties of cross-pollinating plants present more of a problem to the plant breeder and seed producer. Artificial crossing between two selected plants may be used to produce a family which, if selected from over a number of generations, will be reasonable but such uniformity must be maintained by reselection at each generation. In practice such 'variations' are liable to show genetic drift with time and the consequent danger of named cultivars from different sources varying in their performance in the field.

F_1 Hybrids

With the increasing emphasis placed on uniformity in vegetable production there has been a trend towrads the use of F_1 hybrids. By crossing two genetically uniform, but distinct, parent lines, F_1 hybrids are produced possessing the attributes of a high level of uniformity and increased vigour in terms of yield, earlier germination, disease resistance, etc. The success of this method for producing commercial cultivars depends on being able to maintain uniform parent lines and ensuring that the F_1 seed results from a direct cross between the two selected parents only. The parent lines are normally self-incompatible, thus making cross-pollination essential for F_1 production. In practice the self-incompatibility mechanism may not be entirely successful and a low level of self-pollination may occur resulting in the production of a small percentage of sibling production. The resulting 'sibs' as they are known, are readily identifiable and provided that they are only present in small numbers need not present too much of a problem.

Other mechanisms adopted in the production of F_1 hybrids include the use of male sterile female plants for seed production and in some instances the emasculation of the seed bearing plant by hand, a process which results in increased production costs.

The maintenance of the inbred parent lines presents a problem, particularly when these have high levels of self-incompatibility, but the development of vegetative propagation techniques including tissue culture is likely to be more widely used for this purpose in the future.

Synthetic cultivars

The cost of production of F_1 hybrid seed is of course much higher than that of conventional mass-pollinated cultivars. If instead of producing F_1 hybrid seed from only two specific inbred parents, a number of such genetically uniform inbred lines are grown together, then random cross-pollination will occur thus producing a mixed hybrid seed. Many combinations of inbred lines and varying numbers of plants within them may be used, the resultant seed being referred to as a synthetic hybrid. In this way the costs of production are reduced but at the expense of some loss in uniformity compared with F_1 hybrid seed production.

Establishing a new cultivar

It will be apparent from the foregoing outline of plant breeding methods, that it may take several years to produce a new vegetable cultivar, during which it must undergo a number of different multiplication and testing procedures before release to growers. Such tests are designed to ensure that the new introduction is in fact different from existing cultivars and sufficiently uniform and stable to be reproduced over successive multiplications. Most countries will have their own organisation for conducting such tests; in the United Kingdom they are carried out by the National Institute of Botany (N.I.A.B.) at Cambridge. Once the cultivar has been accepted as new it can be registered on the National List of Vegetables and also added to the European Economic Community's Common Catalogue of Vegetable Varieties. Until it is registered in this way it may not be sold within the E.E.C. Provision must also be made for it to be maintained in such a way that it remains true to type.

Similar criteria are also used by the Plant Breeder's Right Scheme which ensures that, at least for many species, a breeder can obtain an agreed royalty payment on the sale of seed for any new cultivar he may have produced.

Plant breeding in practice may be carried out by many organisations including state research stations, commercial seed companies and perhaps to a lesser extent in the case of vegetables, by private individuals.

The maintenance and production of vegetable seed

Once a new cultivar has been precisely defined and accepted it must be maintained. In the case of self-pollinated species this is relatively easy as the isolation of breeding material is less important. However, a level of mass-selection is desirable to maintain the original characteristics of a cultivar.

Cross-pollinated species, however, require that seed production areas are carefully isolated from other plants of the same species and vigorous plant selection is vital to maintaining purity of the line. Care should be taken to ensure that such selection is carried out with reference to the original description in order to prevent the development of a different type or cultivar.

Seed carefully maintained in this way is referred to as pre-basic seed. If on testing it is found to be true to type then it can be used to produce 'basic' seed which can then be bulked up for commercial use. If the seed crops are inspected during growth by a relevant authority, such as the N.I.A.B., they are graded as certified seed, otherwise they are referred to as standard seed.

Progeny testing is also desirable during the early stages of seed production. The method involves the seeding together of selected plants, harvesting the seed from each separately and then growing on small samples of this seed to identify the superior progenies. It is then possible to bulk up the remaining seed corresponding to those selected progenies and also to use the selected plants for further seed production.

Seed production in polythene tunnels

The plot isolation which is particularly important in the production of seed from cross-pollinated species is traditionally achieved by growing plants in areas in which similar plants are not grown. Ideally such areas should also be in regions where the summer rainfall is low so that seed maturity and ripening can take place successfully.

At least in the early stages of bulking up seed it is possible to provide the necessary conditions in plastic tunnels provided with screened doors and ventilators to prevent the entry of pollinating insects. This approach is now used by the National Vegetable Research Station, U.K., where blowflies are used as pollinators and are preferred to honey bees because of their more random feeding habits. It has been shown that in the case of F_1 hybrid production the resulting random pollination results in reduced sibling production compared with that in the case of honey bee activity where the insects systematically visit several flowers on the same plant thus increasing the possibility of self-pollination (Faulkner and Hinton, 1980).

Commercial seed production
Commercial seed production is usually carried out in warmer countries although a number of vegetable species are biennials and require exposure to cold temperatures for vernalisation. Provision must also be made for crop inspection at various stages during the growth of the seed crop.

Following harvest the plants must go through a process of drying prior to threshing and seed cleaning and grading. Seed must also be tested and stored under suitable conditions until marketed.

Seed testing
Legislation exists in many countries to protect the vegetable grower against variations in standards of purity, germination and weed seed content. The minimum analytical purity indicating the percentage by weight of pure seed in tested samples may range from as low as 95% for small seeded vegetables such as lettuce and carrot to 98% for large seeded species such as peas and beans. There are separate levels specified for minimum percentage of seed of other species ranging from values of 1 to 1.5% for small seeded vegetables which are more difficult to clean down to as low as 0.1% for larger species.

Germination capacity varies between different seed lots of a particular vegetable and laboratory testing is used to determine performance under standard conditions. The results allow growers and seed merchants to assess the germination quality of different samples. International seed testing is administered and coordinated by the International Seed Testing Committee which defines and regularly re-assesses the detailed rules and procedures (International

Seed Testing Association, 1976). Purity tests are included to determine the quantity of impurities and national organisations use the germination and purity figures to enforce minimum standards for seed that is sold. The germination standards which apply in the European Economic Community (E.E.C.) are shown in table 12.2.

Table 12.2   E.E.C. statutory minimum levels of germination for some vegetable seeds

Minimum not specified	65%	70%	75%	80%
Parsnip	Carrot	Asparagus	Bean, French	Bean, broad
	Chicory	Beetroot	Brussels sprout	Bean, runner
	Endive	Cauliflower	Cabbage	Pea
	Leek	Celery	Lettuce	Turnip
	Parsley	Maize	Marrow	
		Onion	Spinach	
		Radish	Tomato	

Germination tests are normally carried out on natural seed before any chemical treatments are applied but techniques are also available for testing pelleted seeds. Laboratory germination testing indicates the capacity of a particular seed lot to produce normal plants in the field. Recording of germinated seeds is only done when it is clear that the seedlings are not damaged, deformed or decayed.

An important aspect of seed performance in the field is that of seed vigour for which there is currently no legislation. Seed germination is relatively easy to define and measure but it is more of a problem to define seed vigour and although there are a number of vigour tests none has been universally accepted. The International Seed Testing Association defines seed vigour as 'the total of those properties of the seed which determine the potential level of activity and performance of the seed or seed lot during germination and seedling emergence'.

Laboratory germination tests are intended as a guide to the performance of seeds when they are grown in good soil conditions but field performance and emergence are usually considerably worse than the laboratory results. The concept of seed vigour is used to explain field difference of seed lots with identical laboratory performances. Seed with high germination percentages usually gives good field establishment but seed ageing, caused particularly by high temperatures and humidities, results in severe and unpredictable reductions in emergence. This is particularly serious when the necessary programmed plant populations cannot be achieved for processing crops such as carrots, beetroot, Brussels sprouts, etc.

Seeds can be classified into vigour categories ranging from low to high. Low vigour seeds give low field emergence which is worst in adverse soil conditions such as low temperature (e.g. carrots) or excessive moisture content (e.g. beetroot). Reductions in emergence caused by soil pathogens are also more marked with low vigour seed. High and medium vigour seeds perform better but close correlations between laboratory germination and likely field emergence can only be drawn when field conditions are most favourable.

Vigour tests have been devised for maize (Heydecker, 1969) and for peas (Mathews and Bradnock, 1967) while workers at the Scottish Horticultural Research Institute have postulated a relationship between laboratory germination of carrots at 10°C and field emergence (Hegarty, 1971). The pea vigour test involves measuring the electroconductivity of the water in which seeds have been soaked for twenty-four hours. Leachate from the highest vigour seeds, which produce the best field emergence, gives the lowest electroconductivity readings.

Methods of evaluating seed vigour in carrots have included a controlled deterioration technique (Mathews, 1980) in which seeds are first 'aged' by storing them for short periods at high temperatures and moisture content prior to testing germination in the standard way. Comparison of embryo length in carrot seed has also been demonstrated to be a useful guide to field performance (Gray and Steckel, 1983a). The development of reliable vigour tests for other vegetable species would enable the grower to select seed of quality for his own particular production system.

Many factors can influence the level of vigour in a seed sample including, for example, the effect of environmental conditions on the parent plant. Research on carrots has demonstrated the importance of seed position on the parent plants in determining subsequent performance and seeds from the primary umbel will emerge more rapidly and uniformly following sowing than those from higher order umbels. The carrot seed producer is able to increase the proportion of primary umbels in his seed crop by using high density plants and can also affect the quality of seed through choice of harvest date and seed grading (Gray and Steckel, 1983b).

Seed processing

The seed producer may carry out a number of treatments to his harvested seed prior to marketing. Following drying and preliminary cleaning to remove other plant parts and soil, etc., the most commonly adopted operation is to size grade seed. This will contribute towards more uniform germination within seed lots and allows for any particularly small grades to be rejected.

Vegetable seed is size graded according to a Seed Trade Association/Agricultural Engineers Association scale. It assumes that seeds are spherical, or more or less so, and an alphabetical notation is used for each grade within which a size variation of 0.25 mm is permissible. The scale is shown in table 12.3.

Table 12.3 Seed size grades

Code letter	Size range (mm)	Code letter	Size range (mm)	Code letter	Size range (mm)	Code letter	Size range (mm)
A	0 −0.25	G	1.50–1.75	N	3.00–3.25	U	4.50–4.75
B	0.25–0.50	H	1.75–2.00	P	3.25–3.50	V	4.75–5.00
C	0.50–0.75	J	2.00–2.25	Q	3.50–3.75	W	5.00–5.25
D	0.75–1.00	K	2.25–2.50	R	3.75–4.00	X	5.25–5.50
E	1.00–1.25	L	2.50–2.75	S	4.00–4.25	Y	5.50–5.75
F	1.25–1.50	M	2.75–3.00	T	4.25–4.50	Z	5.75–6.00

Size-graded seed is normally available from seedsmen but usually costs at least twice as much as ungraded seed. Brassica seed is graded as G, H or J with approximately 4 000, 3 000 and 2 300 seeds per 10g. Leek seed may be graded as H or J with 4 000 or 3 200 seeds per 10g. Precise seed counts are required for seeding rate calculations.

Seed may also be soaked, or coated in insecticide or fungicide, fumigated against eelworm or pelleted to produce more regular shaped units for precision drilling (see chapter 4). In the case of species such as beetroot which form seed clusters these can be made more uniform and regular in shape by rubbing.

In some instances such pre-treatments may have an adverse effect on subsequent germination and it should be noted that legislation on levels of seed germination refers to seed lots prior to such treatments.

Much research has been carried out on pre-treating and priming seeds to improve their vigour or overcome dormancy thus accelerating seedling emergence. Such techniques are likely to play an important part in precision growing of vegetable crops in the future but to date are not normally carried out by seed producers.

Seed storage

Seed deterioration begins on the parent plant and is accelerated by pest or disease attack, mechanical damage and high temperatures but seed moisture content and temperature are the most important factors which influence longevity.

It is estimated that (a) each 1% reduction in seed moisture content from 14% to 5% will double the life of the seed and (b) each 5°C rise in seed temperature above 0°C halves longevity. These are broad generalisations but it is clear that controlled environment storage conditions are particularly vital in hot, humid countries. The rate of seed deterioration varies with different vegetables. Parsnip, lettuce and onions can deteriorate three times more rapidly than brassicas and tomatoes when stored at ambient temperatures and relative humidities.

The ideal method of storage involves drying the seeds down to 5–6% moisture content and keeping them in sealed moisture-proof containers at low temperature (10°C) and relative humidity (45%).

References and further reading

Allard, R.W. (1960) *Principles of Plant Breeding*. London: Wiley.

Anon. (1979) *The Vegetable Seeds Regulations 1979*. Statutory Instrument No. 744. London: H.M.S.O.

Astley, D. and Lockett, A.H. (1981) 'Vegetable gene bank'. *National Vegetable Research Station annual Report for 1980*, p. 62.

Faulkner, G.J. (1983) *Maintenance, testing and seed production of vegetable stocks at the National Vegetable Research Station*. National Vegetable Research Trust, Wellesbourne, Warwick, England.

Faulkner, G.J. and Hinton, W.L. (1980) 'F₁ hybrid Brussels sprout seed: an assessment of production methods and their economic viability'. *Horticultural Research*, **20**, 49–59.

Gray, D. and Steckel, J.R.A. (1983a) 'A comparison of methods for evaluating seed quality in carrots (*Daucus carota*)'. *Annals of Applied Biology*, **103**, 327–334.

Gray, D. and Steckel, J.R.A. (1983b) 'Seed quality in carrots: the effects of seed crop plant density, harvest date and seed grading on seed and seedling variability'. *Journal of Horticultural Science*, **58**, 393–401.

Hebblethwaite, P.D., ed., (1980) *Seed Production*. London: Butterworths.

Hegarty, T.W. (1971) 'A relation between field emergence and laboratory germination'. *Journal of Horticultural Science*, **46**, 299–305.

Heydecker, W. (1969) 'The vigour of seeds – a review'. *Proceedings of the International Seed Testing Association*, **34**, 201–219.

International Seed Testing Association (1976) 'International rules for seed testing'. *Seed Science and Technology*, **4**, 3–177.

Mathews, S. (1980) 'Controlled deterioration: a new vigour test for crop seeds'. In *Seed Production*, ed. P.D. Hebblethwaite, London: Butterworths, pp. 647–660.

Mathews, S. and Bradnock, W.T. (1967) 'The detection of seed samples of wrinkled-seeded peas (*Pisum sativum* L.) of potentially low planting value'. *Proceedings of the International Seed Testing Association*, **32**, 553–563.

Russell, G.E. (1978) *Plant Breeding for Pest and Disease Resistance*. London: Butterworths.

Simmonds, N.W. (1979) *Principles of Crop Improvement*. London: Longman.

Thompson, J.R. (1979) *An Introduction to Seed Technology*. Glasgow: Leonard Hill.

Watts, L. (1980) *Flower and Vegetable Plant Breeding*. London: Grower Books.

Williams, W. (1964) *Genetical Principles and Plant Breeding*. Oxford: Blackwell.

Appendix: Scientific names of vegetables referred to in the text

Common names of vegetables have been used throughout the text. This appendix is included for readers who may not be acquainted with the crops referred to or who come from areas where different common names are in use.

Artichoke, globe	*Cynara scolymus*
Artichoke, Jerusalem	*Helianthus tuberosus*
Asparagus	*Asparagus officinalis*
Aubergine	*Solanum melangena*
Bean, broad	*Vicia faba*
Bean, French	*Phaseolus vulgaris*
Bean, runner	*Phaseolus coccineus*
Beetroot	*Beta vulgaris*
Broccoli (also known as calabrese, in some regions the term is used to describe winter hardy cauliflower)	*Brassica oleracea* var. *italica*
Brussels sprout	*Brassica oleracea* var. *gemmifera*
Cabbage	*Brassica oleracea* var. *capitata*
Calabrese (see Broccoli)	
Carrot	*Daucus carota*
Cauliflower	*Brassica oleracea* var. *botrytis*
Celeriac (a term used to describe cultivars of celery selected for their swollen shoot base)	
Celery	*Apium graveolens*
Chicory	*Cichorium intybus*
Courgettes (see Marrow)	
Cucumber	*Cucumis sativus*

Garlic	*Allium sativum*
Gourd	*Cucurbita spp.*
Horseradish	*Armoracia rusticana*
Leek	*Allium ampeloprasum*
Lettuce	*Lactuca sativa*
Maize (cultivars harvested immature for their high sugar content are referred to as sweet corn)	*Zea mays*
Marrow	*Cucurbita pepo*
Melon	*Cucumis melo*
Mint	*Mentha spicata*
Mushroom	*Agaricus bisporus*
Onion	*Allium cepa*
Parsnip	*Pastinaca sativa*
Pea	*Pisum sativum*
Pepper	*Capsicum annuum*
Potato (also referred to as Irish potato)	*Solanum tuberosum*
Potato, sweet	*Ipomoea batatus*
Radish	*Rhaphanus sativus*
Rhubarb	*Rheum rhaponticum*
Seakale	*Crambe maritima*
Shallot	*Allium cepa* var. *aggregatum*
Spinach	*Spinacia oleracea*
Sweet corn (see Maize)	
Thyme	*Thymus vulgaris*
Tomato	*Lycopersicon lycoperiscum*
Turnip	*Brassica rapa*
Watercress	*Nasturtium officinale*

Index